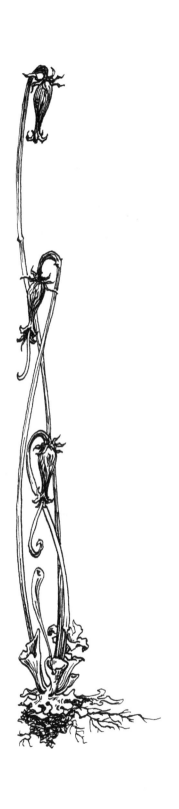

Fungi
from
Yuggoth

H. P. Lovecraft

Fungi from

Yuggoth

AN ANNOTATED EDITION

Edited by David E. Schultz
Illustrated by Jason C. Eckhardt

Hippocampus Press

New York

Published by Hippocampus Press
P.O. Box 641, New York, NY 10156
www.hippocampuspress.com

The text of *Fungi from Yuggoth* is published by permission of the Estate of
H. P. Lovecraft and John Hay Library, Brown University.

Cover and interior illustrations by Jason C. Eckhardt.
Cover design by Dan Sauer, dansauerdesign.com.
Hippocampus Press logo designed by Anastasia Damianakos.

First Paperback Edition, 2022
1 3 5 7 9 8 6 4 2

ISBN 978-0-9721644-7-4

To S. T. Joshi

Contents

Fungi from Yuggoth

I. The Book

Fungi from Yuggoth

The place was dark and dusty and half-lost
In tangles of old alleys near the quays,
Reeking of strange things brought in from the seas,
And with queer curls of fog that west winds tossed.
Small lozenge panes, obscured by smoke and frost,
Just shewed the books, in piles like twisted trees,
Rotting from floor to roof—congeries
Of crumbling elder lore at little cost.

I entered, charmed, and from a cobwebbed heap
Took up the nearest tome and thumbed it through,
Trembling at curious words that seemed to keep
Some secret, monstrous if one only knew.
Then, looking for some seller old in craft,
I could find nothing but a voice that laughed.

II. Pursuit

Fungi from Yuggoth

I held the book beneath my coat, at pains
To hide the thing from sight in such a place;
Hurrying through the ancient harbour lanes
With often-turning head and nervous pace.
Dull, furtive windows in old tottering brick
Peered at me oddly as I hastened by,
And thinking what they sheltered, I grew sick
For a redeeming glimpse of clean blue sky.

No one had seen me take the thing—but still
A blank laugh echoed in my whirling head,
And I could guess what nighted worlds of ill
Lurked in that volume I had coveted.
The way grew strange—the walls alike and madding—
And far behind me, unseen feet were padding.

III. THE KEY

Fungi from Yuggoth

I do not know what windings in the waste
Of those strange sea-lanes brought me home once more,
But on my porch I trembled, white with haste
To get inside and bolt the heavy door.
I had the book that told the hidden way
Across the void and through the space-hung screens
That hold the undimensioned worlds at bay,
And keep lost aeons to their own demesnes.

At last the key was mine to those vague visions
Of sunset spires and twilight woods that brood
Dim in the gulfs beyond this earth's precisions,
Lurking as memories of infinitude.
The key was mine, but as I sat there mumbling,
The attic window shook with a faint fumbling.

IV. Recognition

Fungi from Yuggoth

The day had come again, when as a child
I saw—just once—that hollow of old oaks,
Grey with a ground-mist that enfolds and chokes
The slinking shapes which madness has defiled.
It was the same—an herbage rank and wild
Clings round an altar whose carved sign invokes
That Nameless One to whom a thousand smokes
Rose, aeons gone, from unclean towers up-piled.

I saw the body spread on that dank stone,
And knew those things which feasted were not men;
I knew this strange, grey world was not my own,
But Yuggoth, past the starry voids—and then
The body shrieked at me with a dead cry,
And all too late I knew that it was I!

V. Homecoming

Fungi from Yuggoth

The daemon said that he would take me home
To the pale, shadowy land I half-recalled
As a high place of stair and terrace, walled
With marble balustrades that sky-winds comb,
While miles below a maze of dome on dome
And tower on tower beside a sea lies sprawled.
Once more, he told me, I would stand enthralled
On those old heights, and hear the far-off foam.

All this he promised, and through sunset's gate
He swept me, past the lapping lakes of flame,
And red-gold thrones of gods without a name
Who shriek in fear at some impending fate.
Then a black gulf with sea-sounds in the night:
"Here was your home", he mocked, "when you had sight!"

VI. The Lamp

Fungi from Yuggoth

We found the lamp inside those hollow cliffs
Whose chiselled sign no prieſt in Thebes could read,
And from whose caverns frightened hieroglyphs
Warned every living creature of earth's breed.
No more was there—juſt that one brazen bowl
With traces of a curious oil within;
Fretted with some obscurely-patterned scroll,
And symbols hinting vaguely of ſtrange sin.

Little the fears of forty centuries meant
To us as we bore off our slender spoil,
And when we scanned it in our darkened tent
We ſtruck a match to teſt the ancient oil.
It blazed—great God! . . . But the vaſt shapes we saw
In that mad flash have seared our lives with awe.

VII. Zaman's Hill

Fungi from Yuggoth

The great hill hung close over the old town,
A precipice against the main street's end;
Green, tall, and wooded, looking darkly down
Upon the steeple at the highway bend.
Two hundred years the whispers had been heard
About what happened on the man-shunned slope—
Tales of an oddly mangled deer or bird,
Or of lost boys whose kin had ceased to hope.

One day the mail-man found no village there,
Nor were its folk or houses seen again;
People came out from Aylesbury to stare—
Yet they all told the mail-man it was plain
That he was mad for saying he had spied
The great hill's gluttonous eyes, and jaws stretched wide.

VIII. THE PORT

Fungi from Yuggoth

Ten miles from Arkham I had struck the trail
That rides the cliff-edge over Boynton Beach,
And hoped that just at sunset I could reach
The crest that looks on Innsmouth in the vale.
Far out at sea was a retreating sail,
White as hard years of ancient winds could bleach,
But evil with some portent beyond speech,
So that I did not wave my hand or hail.

Sails out of Innsmouth! echoing old renown
Of long-dead times. But now a too-swift night
Is closing in, and I have reached the height
Whence I so often scan the distant town.
The spires and roofs are there—but look! The gloom
Sinks on dark lanes, as lightless as the tomb!

IX. The Courtyard

Fungi from Yuggoth

It was the city I had known before;
The ancient, leprous town where mongrel throngs
Chant to strange gods, and beat unhallowed gongs
In crypts beneath foul alleys near the shore.
The rotting, fish-eyed houses leered at me
From where they leaned, drunk and half-animate,
As edging through the filth I passed the gate
To the black courtyard where the man would be.

The dark walls closed me in, and loud I cursed
That ever I had come to such a den,
When suddenly a score of windows burst
Into wild light, and swarmed with dancing men:
Mad, soundless revels of the dragging dead—
And not a corpse had either hands or head!

X. THE PIGEON~FLYERS

Fungi from Yuggoth

They took me slumming, where gaunt walls of brick
Bulge outward with a viscous stored-up evil,
And twisted faces, thronging foul and thick,
Wink messages to alien god and devil.
A million fires were blazing in the streets,
And from flat roofs a furtive few would fly
Bedraggled birds into the yawning sky
While hidden drums droned on with measured beats.

I knew those fires were brewing monstrous things,
And that those birds of space had been *Outside*—
I guessed to what dark planet's crypts they plied,
And what they brought from Thog beneath their wings.
The others laughed—till struck too mute to speak
By what they glimpsed in one bird's evil beak.

XI. The Well

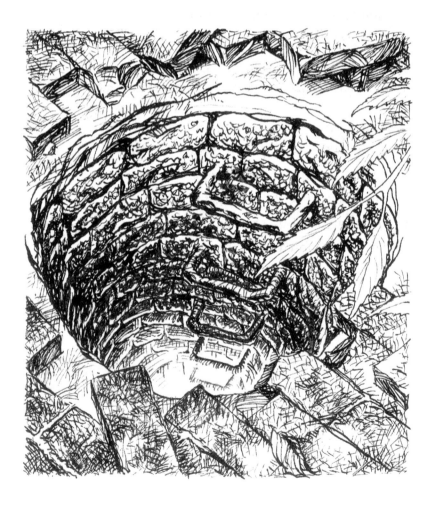

Fungi from Yuggoth

Farmer Seth Atwood was past eighty when
He tried to sink that deep well by his door,
With only Eb to help him bore and bore.
We laughed, and hoped he'd soon be sane again.
And yet, instead, young Eb went crazy, too,
So that they shipped him to the county farm.
Seth bricked the well-mouth up as tight as glue—
Then hacked an artery in his gnarled left arm.

After the funeral we felt bound to get
Out to that well and rip the bricks away,
But all we saw were iron hand-holds set
Down a black hole deeper than we could say.
And yet we put the bricks back—for we found
The hole too deep for any line to sound.

XII. The Howler

Fungi from Yuggoth

They told me not to take the Briggs' Hill path
That used to be the highroad through to Zoar,
For Goody Watkins, hanged in seventeen-four,
Had left a certain monstrous aftermath.
Yet when I disobeyed, and had in view
The vine-hung cottage by the great rock slope,
I could not think of elms or hempen rope,
But wondered why the house still seemed so new.

Stopping a while to watch the fading day,
I heard faint howls, as from a room upstairs,
When through the ivied panes one sunset ray
Struck in, and caught the howler unawares.
I glimpsed—and ran in frenzy from the place,
And from a four-pawed thing with human face.

XIII. Hesperia

Fungi from Yuggoth

The winter sunset, flaming beyond spires
And chimneys half-detached from this dull sphere,
Opens great gates to some forgotten year
Of elder splendours and divine desires.
Expectant wonders burn in those rich fires,
Adventure-fraught, and not untinged with fear;
A row of sphinxes where the way leads clear
Toward walls and turrets quivering to far lyres.

It is the land where beauty's meaning flowers;
Where every unplaced memory has a source;
Where the great river Time begins its course
Down the vast void in starlit streams of hours.
Dreams bring us close—but ancient lore repeats
That human tread has never soiled these streets.

XIV. Star-Winds

Fungi from Yuggoth

It is a certain hour of twilight glooms,
Mostly in autumn, when the star-wind pours
Down hilltop streets, deserted out-of-doors,
But shewing early lamplight from snug rooms.
The dead leaves rush in strange, fantastic twists,
And chimney-smoke whirls round with alien grace,
Heeding geometries of outer space,
While Fomalhaut peers in through southward mists.

This is the hour when moonstruck poets know
What fungi sprout in Yuggoth, and what scents
And tints of flowers fill Nithon's continents,
Such as in no poor earthly garden blow.
Yet for each dream these winds to us convey,
A dozen more of ours they sweep away!

XV. Antarktos

Fungi from Yuggoth

Deep in my dream the great bird whispered queerly
Of the black cone amid the polar waſte;
Pushing above the ice-sheet lone and drearly,
By ſtorm-crazed aeons battered and defaced.
Hither no living earth-shapes take their courses,
And only pale auroras and faint suns
Glow on that pitted rock, whose primal sources
Are guessed at dimly by the Elder Ones.

If men should glimpse it, they would merely wonder
What tricky mound of Nature's build they spied;
But the bird told of vaſter parts, that under
The mile-deep ice-shroud crouch and brood and bide.
God help the dreamer whose mad visions shew
Those dead eyes set in cryſtal gulfs below!

XVI. The Window

Fungi from Yuggoth

The house was old, with tangled wings outthrown,
Of which no one could ever half keep track,
And in a small room somewhat near the back
Was an odd window sealed with ancient stone.
There, in a dream-plagued childhood, quite alone
I used to go, where night reigned vague and black;
Parting the cobwebs with a curious lack
Of fear, and with a wonder each time grown.

One later day I brought the masons there
To find what view my dim forbears had shunned,
But as they pierced the stone, a rush of air
Burst from the alien voids that yawned beyond.
They fled—but I peered through and found unrolled
All the wild worlds of which my dreams had told.

XVII. A Memory

Fungi from Yuggoth

There were great steppes, and rocky table-lands
Stretching half-limitless in starlit night,
With alien campfires shedding feeble light
On beasts with tinkling bells, in shaggy bands.
Far to the south the plain sloped low and wide
To a dark zigzag line of wall that lay
Like a huge python of some primal day
Which endless time had chilled and petrified.

I shivered oddly in the cold, thin air,
And wondered where I was and how I came,
When a cloaked form against a campfire's glare
Rose and approached, and called me by my name.
Staring at that dead face beneath the hood,
I ceased to hope—because I understood.

XVIII. The Gardens of Yin

Fungi from Yuggoth

Beyond that wall, whose ancient masonry
Reached almost to the sky in moss-thick towers,
There would be terraced gardens, rich with flowers,
And flutter of bird and butterfly and bee.
There would be walks, and bridges arching over
Warm lotos-pools reflecting temple eaves,
And cherry-trees with delicate boughs and leaves
Against a pink sky where the herons hover.

All would be there, for had not old dreams flung
Open the gate to that stone-lanterned maze
Where drowsy streams spin out their winding ways,
Trailed by green vines from bending branches hung?
I hurried—but when the wall rose, grim and great,
I found there was no longer any gate.

XIX. The Bells

Fungi from Yuggoth

Year after year I heard that faint, far ringing
Of deep-toned bells on the black midnight wind;
Peals from no steeple I could ever find,
But strange, as if across some great void winging.
I searched my dreams and memories for a clue,
And thought of all the chimes my visions carried;
Of quiet Innsmouth, where the white gulls tarried
Around an ancient spire that once I knew.

Always perplexed I heard those far notes falling,
Till one March night the bleak rain splashing cold
Beckoned me back through gateways of recalling
To elder towers where the mad clappers tolled.
They tolled—but from the sunless tides that pour
Through sunken valleys on the sea's dead floor.

XX. NIGHT~GAUNTS

Fungi from Yuggoth

Out of what crypt they crawl, I cannot tell,
But every night I see the rubbery things,
Black, horned, and slender, with membraneous wings,
And tails that bear the bifid barb of hell.
They come in legions on the north wind's swell,
With obscene clutch that titillates and stings,
Snatching me off on monstrous voyagings
To grey worlds hidden deep in nightmare's well.

Over the jagged peaks of Thok they sweep,
Heedless of all the cries I try to make,
And down the nether pits to that foul lake
Where the puffed shoggoths splash in doubtful sleep.
But oh! If only they would make some sound,
Or wear a face where faces should be found!

XXI. Nyarlathotep

Fungi from Yuggoth

And at the last from inner Egypt came
The strange dark One to whom the fellahs bowed;
Silent and lean and cryptically proud,
And wrapped in fabrics red as sunset flame.
Throngs pressed around, frantic for his commands,
But leaving, could not tell what they had heard;
While through the nations spread the awestruck word
That wild beasts followed him and licked his hands.

Soon from the sea a noxious birth began;
Forgotten lands with weedy spires of gold;
The ground was cleft, and mad auroras rolled
Down on the quaking citadels of man.
Then, crushing what he chanced to mould in play,
The idiot Chaos blew Earth's dust away.

XXII. Azathoth

Fungi from Yuggoth

Out in the mindless void the daemon bore me,
Past the bright clusters of dimensioned space,
Till neither time nor matter stretched before me,
But only Chaos, without form or place.
Here the vast Lord of All in darkness muttered
Things he had dreamed but could not understand,
While near him shapeless bat-things flopped and fluttered
In idiot vortices that ray-streams fanned.

They danced insanely to the high, thin whining
Of a cracked flute clutched in a monstrous paw,
Whence flow the aimless waves whose chance combining
Gives each frail cosmos its eternal law.
"I am His Messenger", the daemon said,
As in contempt he struck his Master's head.

XXIII. Mirage

Fungi from Yuggoth

I do not know if ever it existed—
That lost world floating dimly on Time's stream—
And yet I see it often, violet-misted,
And shimmering at the back of some vague dream.
There were strange towers and curious lapping rivers,
Labyrinths of wonder, and low vaults of light,
And bough-crossed skies of flame, like that which quivers
Wistfully just before a winter's night.

Great moors led off to sedgy shores unpeopled,
Where vast birds wheeled, while on a windswept hill
There was a village, ancient and white-steepled,
With evening chimes for which I listen still.
I do not know what land it is—or dare
Ask when or why I was, or will be, there.

XXIV. THE CANAL

Fungi from Yuggoth

Somewhere in dream there is an evil place
Where tall, deserted buildings crowd along
A deep, black, narrow channel, reeking strong
Of frightful things whence oily currents race.
Lanes with old walls half-meeting overhead
Wind off to streets one may or may not know,
And feeble moonlight sheds a spectral glow
Over long rows of windows, dark and dead.

There are no footfalls, and the one soft sound
Is of the oily water as it glides
Under stone bridges, and along the sides
Of its deep flume, to some vague ocean bound.
None lives to tell when that stream washed away
Its dream-lost region from the world of day.

XXV. St. Toad's

Fungi from Yuggoth

"Beware St. Toad's cracked chimes!" I heard him scream
  As I plunged into those mad lanes that wind
  In labyrinths obscure and undefined
  South of the river where old centuries dream.
  He was a furtive figure, bent and ragged,
  And in a flash had staggered out of sight,
  So still I burrowed onward in the night
  Toward where more roof-lines rose, malign and jagged.

No guide-book told of what was lurking here—
  But now I heard another old man shriek:
  "Beware St. Toad's cracked chimes!" And growing weak,
  I paused, when a third greybeard croaked in fear:
  "Beware St. Toad's cracked chimes!" Aghast, I fled—
  Till suddenly that black spire loomed ahead.

XXVI. The Familiars

Fungi from Yuggoth

John Whateley lived about a mile from town,
Up where the hills begin to huddle thick;
We never thought his wits were very quick,
Seeing the way he let his farm run down.
He used to waste his time on some queer books
He'd found around the attic of his place,
Till funny lines got creased into his face,
And folks all said they didn't like his looks.

When he began those night-howls we declared
He'd better be locked up away from harm,
So three men from the Aylesbury town farm
Went for him—but came back alone and scared.
They'd found him talking to two crouching things
That at their step flew off on great black wings.

XXVII. The Elder Pharos

Fungi from Yuggoth

From Leng, where rocky peaks climb bleak and bare
Under cold stars obscure to human sight,
There shoots at dusk a single beam of light
Whose far blue rays make shepherds whine in prayer.
They say (though none has been there) that it comes
Out of a pharos in a tower of stone,
Where the last Elder One lives on alone,
Talking to Chaos with the beat of drums.

The Thing, they whisper, wears a silken mask
Of yellow, whose queer folds appear to hide
A face not of this earth, though none dares ask
Just what those features are, which bulge inside.
Many, in man's first youth, sought out that glow,
But what they found, no one will ever know.

XXVIII. Expectancy

Fungi from Yuggoth

I cannot tell why some things hold for me
A sense of unplumbed marvels to befall,
Or of a rift in the horizon's wall
Opening to worlds where only gods can be.
There is a breathless, vague expectancy,
As of vast ancient pomps I half-recall,
Or wild adventures, uncorporeal,
Ecstasy-fraught, and as a day-dream free.

It is in sunsets and strange city spires,
Old villages and woods and misty downs,
South winds, the sea, low hills, and lighted towns,
Old gardens, half-heard songs, and the moon's fires.
But though its lure alone makes life worth living,
None gains or guesses what it hints at giving.

XXIX. Nostalgia

Fungi from Yuggoth

Once every year, in autumn's wistful glow,
The birds fly out over an ocean waste,
Calling and chattering in a joyous haste
To reach some land their inner memories know.
Great terraced gardens where bright blossoms blow,
And lines of mangoes luscious to the taste,
And temple-groves with branches interlaced
Over cool paths—all these their vague dreams shew.

They search the sea for marks of their old shore—
For the tall city, white and turreted—
But only empty waters stretch ahead,
So that at last they turn away once more.
Yet sunken deep where alien polyps throng,
The old towers miss their lost, remembered song.

XXX. Background

Fungi from Yuggoth

I never can be tied to raw, new things,
For I first saw the light in an old town,
Where from my window huddled roofs sloped down
To a quaint harbour rich with visionings.
Streets with carved doorways where the sunset beams
Flooded old fanlights and small window-panes,
And Georgian steeples topped with gilded vanes—
These were the sights that shaped my childhood dreams.

Such treasures, left from times of cautious leaven,
Cannot but loose the hold of flimsier wraiths
That flit with shifting ways and muddled faiths
Across the changeless walls of earth and heaven.
They cut the moment's thongs and leave me free
To stand alone before eternity.

XXXI. The Dweller

Fungi from Yuggoth

It had been old when Babylon was new;
None knows how long it slept beneath that mound,
Where in the end our questing shovels found
Its granite blocks and brought it back to view.
There were vast pavements and foundation-walls,
And crumbling slabs and statues, carved to shew
Fantastic beings of some long ago
Past anything the world of man recalls.

And then we saw those stone steps leading down
Through a choked gate of graven dolomite
To some black haven of eternal night
Where elder signs and primal secrets frown.
We cleared a path—but raced in mad retreat
When from below we heard those clumping feet.

XXXII. Alienation

Fungi from Yuggoth

His solid flesh had never been away,
For each dawn found him in his usual place,
But every night his spirit loved to race
Through gulfs and worlds remote from common day.
He had seen Yaddith, yet retained his mind,
And come back safely from the Ghooric zone,
When one still night across curved space was thrown
That beckoning piping from the voids behind.

He waked that morning as an older man,
And nothing since has looked the same to him.
Objects around float nebulous and dim—
False, phantom trifles of some vaster plan.
His folk and friends are now an alien throng
To which he struggles vainly to belong.

XXXIII. Harbour Whistles

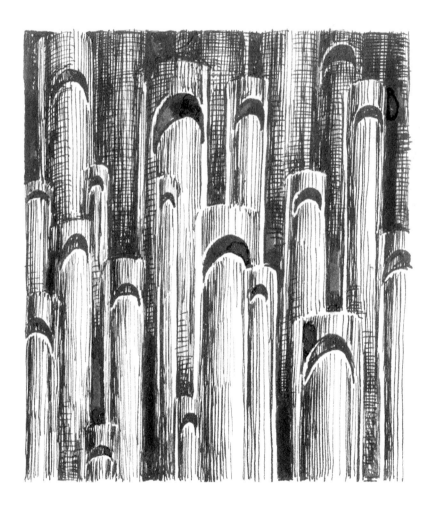

Fungi from Yuggoth

Over old roofs and past decaying spires
The harbour whistles chant all through the night;
Throats from strange ports, and beaches far and white,
And fabulous oceans, ranged in motley choirs.
Each to the other alien and unknown,
Yet all, by some obscurely-focussed force
From brooding gulfs beyond the Zodiac's course,
Fused into one mysterious cosmic drone.

Through shadowy dreams they send a marching line
Of still more shadowy shapes and hints and views;
Echoes from outer voids, and subtle clues
To things which they themselves cannot define.
And always in that chorus, faintly blent,
We catch some notes no earth-ship ever sent.

XXXIV. Recapture

Fungi from Yuggoth

The way led down a dark, half-wooded heath
Where moss-grey boulders humped above the mould,
And curious drops, disquieting and cold,
Sprayed up from unseen streams in gulfs beneath.
There was no wind, nor any trace of sound
In puzzling shrub, or alien-featured tree,
Nor any view before—till suddenly,
Straight in my path, I saw a monstrous mound.

Half to the sky those steep sides loomed upspread,
Rank-grassed, and cluttered by a crumbling flight
Of lava stairs that scaled the fear-topped height
In steps too vast for any human tread.
I shrieked—and *knew* what primal star and year
Had sucked me back from man's dream-transient sphere!

XXXV. Evening Star

Fungi from Yuggoth

I saw it from that hidden, silent place
Where the old wood half shuts the meadow in.
It shone through all the sunset's glories—thin
At first, but with a slowly-brightening face.
Night came, and that lone beacon, amber-hued,
Beat on my sight as never it did of old;
The evening star—but grown a thousandfold
More haunting in this hush and solitude.

It traced strange pictures on the quivering air—
Half-memories that had always filled my eyes—
Vast towers and gardens; curious seas and skies
Of some dim life—I never could tell where.
But now I knew that through the cosmic dome
Those rays were calling from my far, lost home.

XXXVI. Continuity

Fungi from Yuggoth

There is in certain ancient things a trace
Of some dim essence—more than form or weight;
A tenuous aether, indeterminate,
Yet linked with all the laws of time and space.
A faint, veiled sign of continuities
That outward eyes can never quite descry;
Of locked dimensions harbouring years gone by,
And out of reach except for hidden keys.

It moves me most when slanting sunbeams glow
On old farm buildings set against a hill,
And paint with life the shapes which linger still
From centuries less a dream than this we know.
In that strange light I feel I am not far
From the fixt mass whose sides the ages are.

Fungi from Yuggoth

The Manuscript

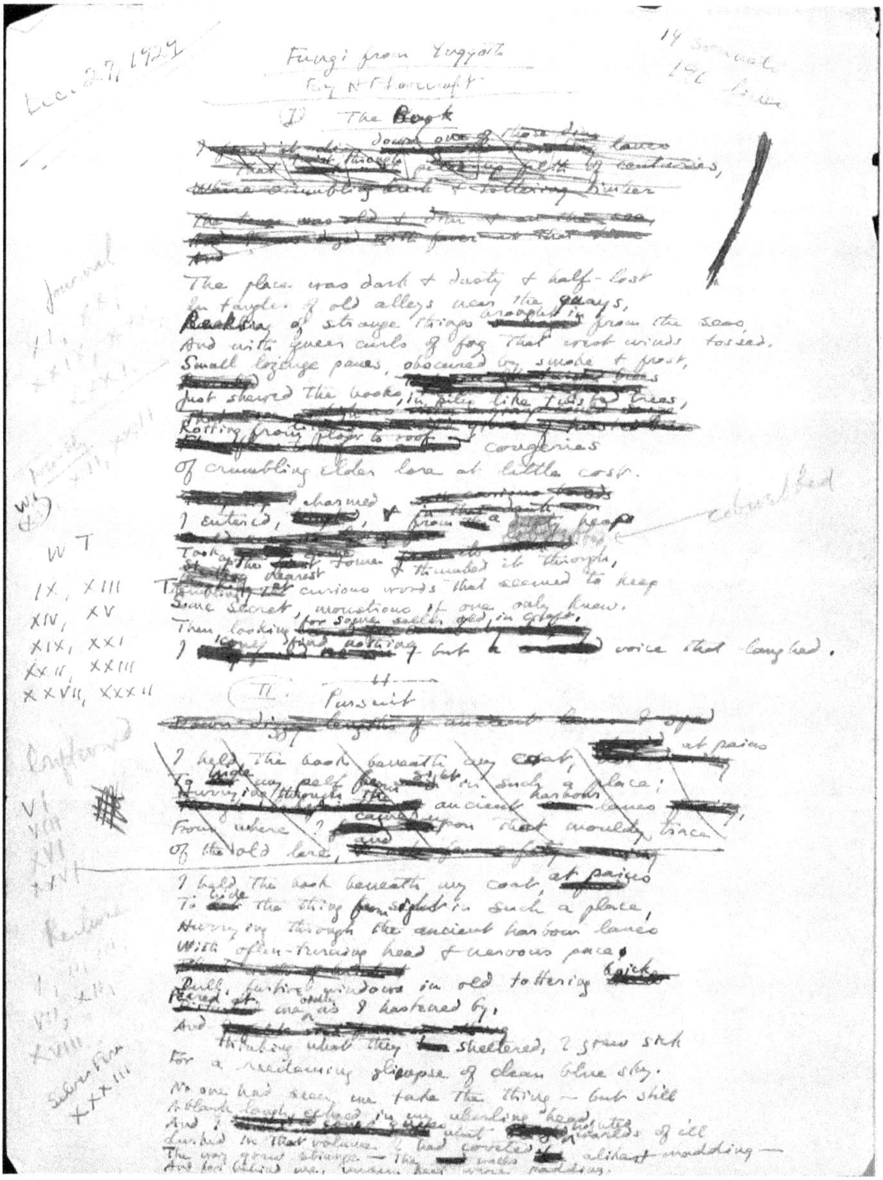

Dec. 27, 1929

Fungi from Yuggoth
By H P Lovecraft

14 Sonnets
196 lines

I The Book

~~That~~ ~~[illegible]~~ ~~centuries,~~
~~Where crumbling brick & tottering timber~~
~~The [illegible] was old & [illegible]~~
~~[illegible]~~
~~And~~

The place was dark & dusty & half-lost
In tangles of old alleys near the quays,
Reeking of strange things brought in from the seas,
And with queer curls of fog that west winds tossed.
Small lozenge panes, obscured by smoke & frost,
Just showed the books, in piles like twisted trees,
Rotting from floor to roof — congeries
Of crumbling elder lore at little cost.
I entered, charmed, & from a cobwebbed heap
Took up the nearest tome & thumbed it through,
Trembling at curious words that seemed to keep
Some secret, monstrous if one only knew.
Then, looking for some seller old in craft,
I could find nothing but a voice that laughed.

II

II Pursuit

~~I held the book beneath my coat, at pains~~
~~To hide my self from sight in such a place;~~
~~Hurrying through the ancient harbour lanes~~
~~From where I came upon that mouldy trace~~
~~Of the old lore,~~

I held the book beneath my coat, at pains
To hide the thing from sight in such a place,
Hurrying through the ancient harbour lanes
With often-turning head & nervous pace.
Dull, furtive windows in old tottering brick
Peered at me oddly as I hastened by,
And thinking what they sheltered, I grew sick
For a redeeming glimpse of clean blue sky.
No one had seen me take the thing — but still
A blank laugh echoed in my whirling head,
And I could guess what nighted worlds of ill
Lurked in that volume I had coveted.
The way grew stranger — the walls alike & maddening —
And far behind me, unseen feet were padding.

Journal
XI, XX, XXIX, XXXI

Weird Tales
IX, XIII
XIV, XV
XIX, XXI
XXII, XXIII
XXVII, XXXII

VI
XVIII
XVI

Silver Fern
XXXIII

III. The Key   2

I do not know what windings in the waste
Of ~~these strange seas~~ ~~through~~ ~~old~~ bore me ~~once~~ more,
But on my ~~porch~~ I trembled, ~~with~~ with haste
To get inside, ~~and~~ half the ~~heavy~~ door.
I had the book that told the hidden ~~way~~ ~~screens~~
Across the void to ~~through~~ ~~their~~ ~~worlds~~ at bay,
That ~~held~~ ~~the~~ ~~at~~ ~~aeons~~ to their ~~below~~ ~~our~~ demesnes.
And ~~keep~~ ~~the~~ ~~they~~ ~~want~~ ~~visions~~
At last ~~these vague~~
~~Of~~ sunset spires, & twilight woods that ~~brood~~
Dim in the ~~gulfs~~ beyond this earth's precincts,
~~Luridly~~ as mem'ries of ~~infinitude~~,
~~The~~ ~~key~~ ~~was~~ ~~but as I sat~~ ~~there~~ ~~mumbling~~,
The ~~attic window~~ shook with a faint grumbling.

IV. Recognition

The day had come again, when as a child
I saw ~~just once~~ that ~~hollow~~ of old oaks,
Grey with ~~ground~~-mist that enfolds & chokes
The slinking shapes which madness has defiled.
It was the same — an herbage rank & wild
Clings round an altar whose carved sign ~~invokes~~
That nameless One to whom a ~~thousand~~ smokes
~~unclean~~ towers up piled.
Rose, aeons gone, ~~from~~ on that ~~dark~~ stone,
I saw the ~~body~~ ~~spread~~
~~Through my~~ ~~upon~~ ~~feasted~~ were not men;
And knew ~~there~~ were not men;
I knew this ~~strange~~ ~~grey~~ ~~world~~ was not my own,
But Yoggoth, past the starry voids — & then
The ~~body~~ shrieked at me with a dead cry,
And ~~too late~~ I knew that it was I.

V. Homecoming

The daemon said that he would take me home
To the ~~pale~~ shadowy land I half-recalled
As a high place of stair & terrace, walled
With marble balustrades that sky-winds comb,
While below a maze of domes on domes
And ~~towers~~ on towers ~~beside~~ ~~all~~ ~~seas~~ ~~lies~~ sprawled
Once more, he told me ~~would stand~~ enthralled
On those old heights, ~~hear~~ the far-off foam.
All this he promised, & through sunset's gate
He swept me, past the lapping ~~seas~~ of flame,
And red-gold thrones of gods without a name
~~What~~ shriek in fear at some impending fate.

The Manuscript

I. The Lamp

They found the lamp in no where Pharaoh's haunt,
~~But in those caverns~~ the upper Nile
Where Theban priests had feared to

Deep in the crypts ~~that~~ Theban priests had ~~shrugged,~~
And warned against in frightened hieroglyphs,
We found the temple of a world unsecured,
~~There was a crypt beneath the other vaults~~
~~that~~
We found the lamp inside those ~~hollow~~ cliffs
~~No priests in Thebes could read;~~
~~chiselled~~ ~~sign~~ no priest ~~frightened~~ in Thebes could read,
And ~~whose~~ ~~cave~~ ~~hieroglyphs~~
Warned every living creature ~~of~~ earth's bread.

~~Those days of forty centuries~~
~~science~~
~~in the~~ ~~crypts~~ ~~beneath~~
~~where Druid hands had~~ ~~present bowl~~
No ~~trace~~ was ~~here~~ — just that over~~written,~~
With ~~tins of a curious oil~~
~~spattered scroll,~~
And symbols hinting vaguely of strange sin.
~~meant~~
~~Little the fears of forty centuries~~
~~To us as we bore off~~ our ~~blunder~~ spoil,
And ~~when~~ we ~~squad~~ it in ~~our~~ land ~~ancient~~
We struck a match to test the ~~ancient~~ oil ~~shapes we saw~~
~~It~~ — great God! ~~But the~~
In that mad flash ~~have~~ seared our lives with ~~curse.~~

VII. Zaman's Hill

The great hill hung close over the old town,
A precipice against the main street's end;
Green, tall, & wooded, looking darkly down
Upon the steeple at the highway's head.
Two hundred years the whispers had been heard
About what ~~happened~~ on the man-shunned slope —
Tales of an oddly mangled deer or bird,
Or of lost boys whose ~~kin had ceased to hope.~~
~~One day the mail-man~~
~~Nor was it~~
~~The came out from~~
~~yes, they all told~~
~~That he was mad for saying he had spyed~~
~~great hills~~ eyes, & jaws stretchd wide.

VIII. "The Port

Ten miles from Arkham I had struck the trail
That rides the cliff-edge over Boynton Beach,
And hoped that just at sunset I could reach
The crest that looks on Innsmouth in the vale.

Far out at sea was a retreating sail,
White as ~~~~ years of ~~~~ beyond speech,
But ~~~~ evil with some portent beyond speech,
So That ~~~~ I dared not wave any hand or hail.

Echoing ~~~~ unknown
Sails out of Innsmouth. But now a too-swift night
Of long-dead ~~~~. But now a too-swift night
Is closing in ~~~~ I have reached the distant town.
Whence I so often scan the distant town.
The spires & roofs are there — but look! The gloom
Sinks on dark lanes, as lightless as the tomb!

IX. The Courtyard

It was the city I had known before,
where ~~~~ willows ~~~~ from distant skies

~~~~ doctors ~~~~ night-black eyes
Of living filth, turn crafty ~~~~ lands adare.
On alien gate that unknown
It was the old, known way to where he dwelt —
He of strange wisdom & still stranger dreams;
I knew ~~~~ where upper stairs

It was the city I had known before,
where ~~~~ villous ~~~~ gods
The ancient, leprous town where monstrous throngs
Chant to strange gods, & beat unhallowed gongs
In crypts beneath foul alleys near the shore.
The rotting, fish-eyed houses ~~~~ water
From where they leaned,
As ~~~~ through the filth I passed the gate
To the ~~~~ courtyard where the man would be.
The dark walls closed me in, & loud I cursed
That ever I had come to such a den,
When suddenly, a score of windows burst
Into wild light, & swarmed with dancing men:
Mad, soundless revels of the dragging dead —
And not a corpse had either hands or head!

(51)

X.   ~~[crossed out]~~   The Pigeon-Flyers.

They took me slumming, where gaunt ~~walls~~ of brick
Bulge outward with a viscous stored-up evil,
And twisted faces, ~~[crossed out]~~ thronging foul & thick,
~~[crossed out]~~ messages to alien god & devil.
A ~~[crossed out]~~ fires were blazing in the streets,
And from flat roofs a furtive few would fly
Bedraggled birds into the ~~[crossed out]~~ ng sky
While hidden drums droned on with measured beats.

I knew those fires were ~~brewing~~ monstrous things ~~[crossed out]~~
And that those birds of space had been Outside—
~~I guessed to what dark planet's crypts they plied,~~
~~And what they brought from Thog beneath their wings.~~
~~[crossed out]~~
~~[crossed out]~~ — ~~till~~ struck too mute to speak
The others laughed
By what they glimpsed in one bird's evil beak.

II

T.T.

Seth
~~Farmer~~ Atwood was past eighty when
He tried to sink that well beside his door;
We laughed to see the old ~~fool~~ bore & bore
With only Tom & Eb so Eb ~~[crossed out]~~
~~They suffered too till one day they were gone,~~
~~[crossed out]~~
No ~~[crossed out]~~ — this ~~[crossed out]~~ soil was ~~[crossed out]~~ stuff,
So ~~[crossed out]~~ would be foolish to keep diggin' on,
~~[crossed out]~~ wholly out of sight;
But Seth grew soft ~~[crossed out]~~
When we asked why he ~~bricked~~ the well ~~[crossed out]~~
And then he went & shot himself one night.
~~[crossed out]~~ the brick ~~[crossed out]~~ that black hole ~~[crossed out]~~

5 ~~They~~ suffered too, till ~~[crossed out]~~ Seth ~~[crossed out]~~
He'd ~~dig enough~~—~~[crossed out]~~ soil was dry as ~~[crossed out]~~
And ~~[crossed out]~~ be dry to ~~[crossed out]~~ out of sight ~~[crossed out]~~ to stay.
But Tom & Eb ~~[crossed out]~~
Seth bricked the well ~~[crossed out]~~ used to give
When we asked why ~~[crossed out]~~
He shot himself & all the folks ~~[crossed out]~~ in
The stony yard to rip the bricks away;
8 ~~[crossed out]~~ steps down a deep pit were all they found—
But 'twas too deep for any line to sound!

Farmer Seth Atwood ~~was past eighty~~ when
He tried to sink that ~~deep well~~ by his door,
~~...~~
With only Eb to help him bore & bore. Also
We laughed, & hoped he'd soon be sane again.
And yet, instead, young Eb went crazy, too,   ← Merritt
So that they shipped him to the county farm.
Seth ~~...~~ as tight as glue. —
Then ~~...~~ his gnarled left arm.
After the funeral we ~~...~~
~~...~~ the ~~...~~
~~...~~ all we ~~saw where~~ ~~...~~
Down a black hole deeper than we could say.
And yet ~~...~~ for we found
The hole too deep for any line to sound.

XII .   The Howler

They told me not to take the Briggs' Hill path
That used to be the highroad through to Zoar,
~~For good, ...~~ in seventeen-four,
~~... aftermath...~~
~~... disturbed ...~~
They cross by, ~~...~~ the great rocky slope.
I ~~...~~ not think of glues or human rope,
~~That in seventeen-four...~~
~~Are old Zill so distinct ...~~ seemed so new.
But wondered why the ~~house...~~
~~...~~ the ~~... failing day,~~
Stopping a while to watch ~~...~~ room upstairs
I heard ~~...~~ from ~~...~~
~~Where through the wood ...~~ sunset ray
Struck ~~...~~
~~... & caught the howler...~~
I glimpsed ~~...~~
~~—~~ & ran in frenzy from the place,
And from a four-pawed thing with human face.

XIII. Hesperia (7.)

The winter sunset, flaming beyond spires
And ~~chimneys~~ half detached from this dull sphere,
Opens great gates to some forgotten year
Of older splendours & divine desires.
~~Expectant wonders~~ burn in these rich fires,
~~Adventures~~ ~~~~ ~~~~ untinged with fear;
~~~~ A row of sphinxes where the way leads clear
~~~~ ~~~~ ~~~~ ~~~~ chains
~~Through~~ ~~~~ ~~~~ that ~~~~
Town walls & turrets quivering to far lyres.

It is the land where beauty's ~~~~ ~~~~ blooms;
Where ~~~~ unplaced ~~~~ ~~~~ ~~~~ ~~source;
Where the great river ~~~~ ~~~~ into course
~~~~ Down the vast ~~~~ in starlit streams of ~~~~

~~~~ ~~~~ — but ~~~~ ~~~~
~~~~ close ~~~~ ~~~~
~~~~ ~~~~ ~~~~ ~~~~
That ~~~~ ~~~~ ~~~~ ~~~~
That human ~~~~ ~~~~ ~~~~
          tread has never ~~~~ ~~~~ streets.
              soiled

XIV. Star-Winds   ~~twilight glooms~~,
          ~~~~ hour of ~~twilight~~
It is a ~~~~ ~~~~ ~~~~
Mostly in autumn, ~~that~~ the star-wind ~~pours~~
Down hilltop streets, desert ~~~~ out-of-doors,
But shewing early lamplight ~~~~ ~~~~ ~~~~,
~~The dead leaves rush~~ ~~~~ ~~~~ fantastic ~~~~,
~~~~ ~~~~ of distant space,
And chimney-smoke ~~~~ in alien ~~curls~~ twists

The dead leaves rush in strange fantastic ~~~~
And chimney-smoke ~~whirls~~ round with alien ~~glare~~,
Heeding geometries of outer space,
While Fomalhaut peers in through southward mists.

~~At~~ ~~~~ ~~~~
This is the hour when ~~moonstruck~~ poets know ~~scents~~
What fungi sprout in Yuggoth, & what ~~~~
~~~~ ~~~~ ~~~~ ~~perfumes~~ fill ~~hidden~~
~~Surge~~ in ~~~~ ~~earthly gardens~~ blow. ~~~~ continents,
~~~~ for each dream ~~these winds~~ ~~~~ ~~~~
~~A dozen~~ more of ours they sweep away.

291

XV. Antarktos

~~Amid the polar ~~ ~~to monstrous girth~~

~~Looms like a black hill ~~ ~~... sky;~~

~~... no stone ... this no-traveversed earth,~~

Deep in my dream the ~~strange~~ great bird whispered queerly
Of the black cone amid the polar waste;
Pushing above the ice-sheet lone & dreary,
By storm-~~crazed~~ aeons battered & defaced,
~~Hither no ... earth-shapes take their courses,~~
And only pale auroras & faint suns
Glow on that pitted ~~place~~ rock, whose primal sources
Are guessed at ~~dimly~~ by the Elder Ones.
                                    merely
If men should ~~...~~ glimpse it, they would wonder
                mound
What tricky ~~...~~ of Nature's 'build they ~~spied~~;
~~I ... with ... lies ...~~
But the bird told of vaster parts, ~~that~~ under
The   fissure.
~~mile-deep ice-shroud crouch & brood & ...~~
God help the dreamer ~~&~~ whose ~~...~~ visions shew
Those dead eyes ~~...~~ in crystal ~~gulfs~~ below!

(9)

XVI. The Window (Begin p. 6

All his sharp life he saw, the smoke like fine
On the plain's rim that meant the far-off hills,
And from the city walls would

Alleys of daylight's end the phantom
Glimmering above the [redacted] of roof-line's edge;
[redacted] there faintly waving sedge
Rose above [redacted] from a great salt bay flung

The house was old, with tangled wings outthrown,
Of which no one could ever half keep track,
And in a small room somewhat near the back
Was an odd window sealed with ancient stone.
There in a dream-plagued childhood, quite alone
I used to go, where night reigned vague & black;
Parting the cobwebs with a curious lack
Of fear, & with a wonder each time grown.

One later day I brought the masons there
[redacted]
To find what view my dim forbears had shunned,
But as they pierced the stone, a rush of air
Burst from the alien voids that yawned beyond.
They fled—but I [redacted]
[redacted] through & found unrolled
All the wild worlds of which my dreams had told.

XVII. ~~[crossed out]~~ A Memory

There were great steppes, & rocky table-lands
Stretching half-limitless in starlit night,
With ~~Italian campfires~~ shedding feeble light
On beasts with tinkling bells, in shaggy bands.
~~Far to the south~~ ~~[crossed out]~~
To a ~~dark~~ ~~[crossed out]~~ plain sloped ~~[crossed out]~~ low & wide
Like a huge ~~zigzag line of~~ wall that lay
Upon ~~endless~~ ~~python~~ ~~[crossed out]~~ some primal day,
Whom endless ~~[crossed out]~~ had chilled & petrified.

I shivered oddly in the cold, thin air,
And wondered ~~[crossed out]~~ where I was & how I came,
When a cloaked form against a campfire's glare
Rose & approached, & called me by my name.
Staring at that dead face beneath the hood,
I ~~ceased~~ to hope — because I understood!

XVIII. The Gardens of Yin

~~There would be gardens in the warm, low valley~~
~~Beyond that ancient wall whose worn stones~~
~~Reached almost to the sky, & magically~~
~~breathe the~~
Beyond that ~~[crossed out]~~ wall, whose ancient ~~dragons~~ ~~[crossed out]~~
Reached almost to the sky in rows of thick towers,
~~There would be terraced gardens~~ rich with flowers,
And ~~flutter of bird~~ & butterfly & bee.
~~[crossed out lines]~~
There would be ~~walks~~ and bridges arching over
Warm lotos-pools reflecting temple eaves,
And ~~cherry-trees~~ with delicate ~~[crossed out]~~ & leaves
Against a pink sky where the ~~herons~~ old ~~[crossed out]~~ dreams flung
~~[crossed out]~~ be there, for had not ~~[crossed out]~~
~~[crossed out]~~ were to
~~open~~ the gate to that stone-lanterned
Where ~~young~~ ~~[crossed out]~~ winding ways,
Trailed by green vines ~~[crossed out]~~ from bending branches hung?
~~[crossed out]~~ but where the wall rose grim & great,
I ~~hurried~~ found there was no longer any gate.

(11.5)

XIX.   The Bells

                    That   ringing
Year after year I heard ~~three~~ faint, far ~~bells~~
Of deep-toned bells on the black midnight wind;
Peals from no steeple I could ever find,
But strange, as if across some great void winging.
I searched my dreams & memories for a ~~clue~~ clue,
And thought of all the chimes my visions carried;

To ~~elder~~ towers where the mad clappers ~~tolled~~.
                                    sunless that pour
They tolled ~~in~~ but ~~only~~ from the tides
Through sunless valleys on the sea's dead floor.

for music in
the
valley bans
where losing
voices sound
memory of lost land

Messenger comes to
lead away

slipping through time-
walled road

"man" strewn to the
thing wearing mask.

distant mts. seen from seaport
plains stretching N & S to great city
Receptive of past   sound?
Evil dweller in hills
(bondage to other planet)

city suddenly
deserts
green meadows
crawl uphill

twilight city—
slimbing shapes
not human

cracked brass organ
notes in sumptuous hall
freedom—lost race

Sabbat—cruel
neighbours in
strange antiplace

XX.   Night-gaunts

Out of what crypt they crawl, I cannot tell,
But every night I see the rubbery things,
Black, horned, & slender, with membraneous wings,
And tails that bear the bifid barb of hell.
They come in legions on the north wind's swell,
With ~~obscene~~ clutch that titillates & stings,
Snatching me off on monstrous voyagings
To grey worlds hidden ~~deep~~ in ~~nightmage's~~ well.

Over the jagged peaks of Thok they sweep,
Heedless of all the ~~cries~~ ~~I try to~~ ~~wade~~
And ~~down the~~ nether pits to that foul lake
Where the puffed shoggoths splash in doubtful sleep.
~~would make some sound~~
But, oh! ~~if~~ ~~they~~ ~~face where faces should be found!~~
Or ~~was a~~

XXI.   Nyarlathotep

~~(crossed out line)~~

And at the last from inner Egypt came
The strange dark One to whom the fellahs bowed;
Silent & ~~proud~~
And ~~wrapt~~ in fabrics red as sunset flame;
~~frantic for his~~
Throngs ~~pressed~~ around,
But ~~leaving,~~ could not tell what they had heard;
While through the ~~nations~~ spread the ~~questful~~ word
That wild beasts followed him & licked his hands.

~~(heavily crossed out circled section)~~

Soon from the sea a noxious birth began;
~~Forgotten~~ lands with weedy spires & gold;
The ground was cleft, & mad auroras rolled
Down on the quaking citadels of man.
Then ~~crushing~~ what he chanced to mould in play,
The idiot Chaos blew earth's dust away.

XXII.   Azathoth   (13.)

Out ~~in the~~ mindless ~~void~~ the daemon ~~~~ bore me,
~~Past dreamed~~ ~~~~ ~~~~
Past the bright ~~~~ clusters of dimensioned space,
Till ~~~~ There ~~~~ before me,
~~But~~ neither ~~time nor~~ ~~matter~~ stretched
But only Chaos, without form or place.
~~He~~ ~~~~ ~~~~ ~~~~ muttered
Here the vast Lord of All ~~in darkness~~
Things he had dreamed but could not understand,
While ~~~~ ~~~~ ~~~~ ~~that things~~ flopped & fluttered
In ~~~~ ~~shapeless~~ vastness That ~~~~ ~~shaesies fanned.~~

They danced ~~insanely~~ to the high thin whining
Of ~~a cracked flute~~ ~~~~ ~~~~
~~~~ ~~~~ ~~~~ ~~~~ ~~~~ continuing
Whence flow ~~the~~ ~~~~ errors whose ~~~~ ~~~~
~~~~ ~~~~ ~~~~ ~~~~
Give ~~~~ each frail cosmos its Eternal law.
"I am His Messenger" the daemon said,
As in contempt he struck his ~~Master's~~ head.

XXIII.   MIRAGE

I do not know if ever it existed — ~~There stream~~
~~That toward floated~~ ~~~~ ~~~~
~~And yet~~ ~~~~ violet-misted,
~~And shimmering~~ at the back of ~~some~~ vague dream.
There were strange towers & curious lapping rivers,
~~~~
~~Labyrinths~~ of wonder, & low vaults of light,
And ~~sky~~-crossed skies of flame, like that which quivers
Wistfully ~~~~ just before a winter's night.

~~~~
~~~~
~~~~
Great moors led off to ~~~~ ~~~~ ~~~~
Where vast birds ~~~~ ~~~~ ~~~~ steepled,
~~~~ ~~~~ ~~~~ ~~~~ I listen still.
~~~~
I do not know ~~~~
~~~~ ~~~~ what law it is — or dare
Ask when or why ~~~~ I was, or will be, there.

XXIV. The Canal

~~There is to ... an ... crowd ... mim~~
~~It ... twilight that ... longing ...~~
~~... flume ...~~
~~in ... meadows reap the old crowd's rising~~
~~they in ... sunset's churning ... there ... swim~~
~~... ... ... the~~

Somewhere in dream there is an evil place
Where tall, deserted buildings crowd along
A deep, black, narrow channel, reeking strong
Of frightful things whence oily currents race.
~~...~~ with old ~~...~~ walls half meeting overhead
~~Lanes ... ...~~
Wind ~~off~~ to streets one ~~may~~ or may not know;
And ~~feeble moonlight~~ sheds a spectral glow
~~...~~ dark & dead.

Over ~~long rows of windows~~, & the ~~...~~ one soft sound
There are no footfalls, & the ~~...~~ glides
Is of the oily water ~~...~~
Under stone bridges, & along the sides
Of its deep flume, to some vague ocean bound.
~~None lives ...~~ to tell ~~...~~ that ~~...~~ stream washed away
~~... ...~~ dream-lost region from the world of day.
~~...~~

~~XXV.~~
~~... I ... wandered through the ancient streets~~
~~They ... when I would ... those I know~~
~~... of the river where the ... say~~
~~of the vague ... that ... bridges say~~
~~knots~~

XXV.   St. Toad's

"Beware St. Toad's cracked chimes!"   I heard him scream
As I plunged into those mad lanes that wind
In labyrinthes obscure & undefined   dream.
South of the river where old centuries
He was a furtive figure bent & ragged,
And in a flash, had staggered out of sight,
So still I burrowed onward in the twilight
Toward where were roof-lines weird, malign & jagged.

No guide-book told of what was lurking here —
But now I heard an old man shriek:
"Beware St. Toad's cracked chimes!"   And growing weak
I paused, when a third   grayheard

"Beware St. Toad's cracked chimes!"   Aghast, I fled
Till   suddenly that black spire loomed ahead.

———— H ————

XXVI.   The Familiars.

John Whateley lived about a mile from town,
Up where the hills begin to huddle thick;
We never thought his wits were very quick,
Seeing the way he let his farm run down.
He used to   his time on   books
He'd found around the attic of his place,
Till   lines got creased into his face,
And   folks   they didn't like his looks.

When he began   we declared

So three   from the Aylesbury town farm
Went   but came back glum & scared

That   when they came
They'd found him   crouching
              at their step flew off on great black wings.
"That

XXVII. The Elder Pharos

...where... ...climb... black & bare,
...rocky... ...to human sight,
Under cold stars...
There shoots at dusk a single beam of light
Whose blue... makes shepherds ...in prayer.
They say (though none has been there) that it comes
Out of a pharos in a tower of stone,
Where the last Elder One lives on alone,
Talking to Chaos with the beat of drums.

The Thing, they ...whisper, wears a silken mask
Of yellow, whose... appear to hide
...no one dares ask
Just what the features are, which bulge inside.

Many, in man's first youth, sought out that glow,
But what they found, no one will ever know.

XXVIII. Expectancy

I cannot tell why some things hold for me
A sense of ... marvels to befall,
Or of ... rift in the horizon's wall
Opening to worlds where only ...
There is a breathless, vague expectancy,
As of vast ... pomps ... half-recall,
Of ... adventures, uncorporeal,
Ecstasy-fraught, & as a day-dream free.

It is in sunsets & strange city spires,
Old villages & woods & misty downs,
South winds, the sea, low hills, & lighted towns,
Old gardens, half-heard ... & the moon's fires.
But though its ... alone makes life worth living,
None gains or guesses what it hints at giving.

XXIX. Nostalgia (17.)

~~autumn's~~ wistful ~~glow,~~
Once every year, in ~~spring is ~~~~going & dreaming~~
The birds fly out over an ocean waste,
~~Calling~~ & chattering in a joyous haste
To reach some land their ~~inner~~ memories know.
~~Great ~~~~canopied~~ gardens where bright blossoms blow,
And ~~groves~~ of mangoes luscious to the taste
And ~~purple~~ groves with branches interlaced
~~Over~~ cool paths — all these their vague dreams show.

They search the sea for masks of their old shore,
For the tall city, white & turreted —
But only empty waters stretch ahead,
So that at last they turn away once more,

Yet, ~~sunken~~ deep where ~~polyps throng,~~

The old towers miss their look, remembered ~~long~~

XXX. Background

~~raw,~~ new
I never can be tied to ~~new~~ things,
For I first saw their light in an old town,
Where from my window huddled roofs sloped down
To a ~~quaint~~ harbour rich with ~~visionings.~~

And ~~steeples~~ ~~twilights~~ catch the tides that drown
~~Flooded~~ ~~twilights~~ & ~~window~~-panes,
And ~~gilded~~ ~~spires~~ topt with ~~gilded~~ vanes —
These were the ~~sights~~ that shaped my childhood dreams.

XXXI. The Dweller

It had been old when Babylon was ~~young~~ new;
None ~~knew how long~~ ~~below a roof from~~ it slept beneath that mound,
Where in the end our questing shovel found
Its ~~monstrous~~ granite blocks & brought it back to view.
There were vast pavements & foundation-walls,
And crumbling slabs & statues, ~~carved to shew~~
~~that~~ ~~metals from old~~
Fantastic beings of some long ago
Past anything the world of man recalls.

And then we saw those stone steps leading down,
~~that pierced in coil some~~
Through ~~that pierced~~ ~~the~~
~~fantastic~~ ~~of greater dolomite~~
Through a ~~chaos gate~~ ~~of eternal~~
To some black ~~shapes of eternal~~
Where elder signals & primal secrets frozen.
~~we paths~~ raced in wrad retreat
We cleared a ~~path~~ but fled in wrad retreat
When from below we heard those clumping feet!

XXXII. Alienation

His solid flesh had never been away,
For each ~~dawn~~ ~~left~~ ~~the~~ ~~curious~~ found him in his usual place,
But every night his spirit ~~used~~ to race
Through gulfs & ~~castly~~ reache from common day.
He had seen ~~Yaddith~~ yet retained his ~~mind~~
And ~~came~~ back safely from ~~the~~
~~some grim~~ from the
~~worlds that~~ ~~chaotic zone~~
When once ~~a still~~ night across ~~curved space~~ was thrown
That beckoning piping from the voids behind.

He waked that morning as an older man,
And nothing since had looked the same to him.
Objects around ~~float~~ tremulous & dim,
~~false fantastic~~
False phantom tricks of some ~~darker~~ plan.
~~Now~~ ~~days to his~~
His ~~fellow~~ & friends are now an alien throng
To which he struggled vainly to belong.

(19.)

~~XXXIII~~. Harbour Whistles

Over [illegible] old roofs ~~from the~~ & past decaying spires
The harbour whistles chant all through the night;
~~Throats from strange ports & [illegible]~~
~~[illegible] fabulous seas & white~~
~~[illegible] coral [illegible], in haunting chants,~~
~~For [illegible] stranges of [illegible] chant in brooding choirs.~~
~~Isles of coral~~

Throats from strange ports & beaches far & white,
And fabulous oceans, ~~ranged~~ in motley choirs.
Each to the other alien & unknown,
~~Yet all half-blended by [illegible] brooding force~~
~~[illegible] focussed from gulfs beyond the Zodiac's course,~~
~~And [illegible]~~
~~[illegible] pattern [illegible]~~
Yet all, ~~by~~ [illegible] focussed force
~~From gulfs~~ [illegible] beyond the Zodiac's course,
Fused into one mysterious cosmic drone.

Yet all, by some obscurely-focussed force
From brooding gulfs beyond the Zodiac's course,

Through shadowy ~~[illegible]~~ dreams they send a marching line
Of ~~[illegible] & [illegible]~~ still more shadowy ~~forms~~ shapes & hints & views;
Echoes ~~from~~ from outer voids, & subtle clues
To things which they themselves cannot define.
~~[illegible]~~
~~[illegible]~~
~~[illegible]~~
~~[illegible]~~ And always in that chorus, faintly blent,
We ~~[illegible]~~ catch some notes no earth-ship ever sent.

Jan. 3, 1930

XXXIV. Evening Star (20)

I saw it from that hidden, silent place
Where the old wood half shuts the meadow in.
It shone through the sunset's...
At first but with a slowly - brightening face.

Evening star - but grown a thousandfold
More haunting in this hush & solitude.

Half-memories...
Vast towers & ...

...some of life - ? never could tell where...
But now I know...
Those rays were calling from my far-lost home.

XXXV. Continuity

There is in certain ancient things a trace

Of some essence...
...tenuous...
yet linked with... of time & space.

A faint, veiled sign of... continuities
That outward eyes can never quite descry;
Of... years gone by,

Old houses...

Forests...

The Manuscript

Recapture.

The way led down a dark, half-wooded heath
Where moss-grown boulders humped above the mould,
And curious drops disquieting & cold,
Spray'd up from unseen streams in gulphs beneath.

There was no wind or any trace of sound
In shrub, or puzzling alien-featured tree,
Nor any view before — Till suddenly,
Straight in my path, I saw a monstrous mound.

Half to the sky those steep sides upspread,
Rank-grass'd, & cluttered by a crumbling flight
Of fear-topt stairs that scal'd the height,
An steps too vast for any human tread.

I shriek'd — & knew what primal star & year
Had suck'd me back from man's transient sphere!

Abbreviations

AG   *Letters to Alfred Galpin and Others* (2020)

AT   *The Ancient Track* (2nd ed. 2013)

CB   *Commonplace Book* (1987) or as in *CE* 5; items cited by number

CE   *Collected Essays* (5 vols.; 2004–06)

CF   *Collected Fiction* (4 vols.; 2015–16)

CLM *Letters to C. L. Moore and Others* (2017)

DS   *Dawnward Spire, Lonely Hill: The Letters of H. P. Lovecraft and Clark Ashton Smith* (2017)

DW   *Letters of H. P. Lovecraft and Donald and Howard Wandrei . . .* (2019)

ES   *Essential Solitude: The Letters of H. P. Lovecraft and August Derleth* (2008)

ET   *Letters to Elizabeth Toldridge and Anne Tillery Renshaw* (2014)

FLB   *Letters to F. Lee Baldwin, Duane W. Rimel, and Nils Frome* (2016)

JFM   *Letters to James F. Morton* (2011)

JVS   *Letters to J. Vernon Shea, Carl F. Strauch, and Lee McBride White* (2016)

LFF   *Letters to Family and Family Friends* (2020)

LL   *Lovecraft's Library* (4th ed. 2017)

MF   *A Means to Freedom: The Letters of H. P. Lovecraft and Robert E. Howard* (2009)

ML   *Miscellaneous Letters* (2022)

MWM *Letters to Maurice W. Moe and Others* (2018)

OFF   *O Fortunate Floridian: H. P. Lovecraft's Letters to R. H. Barlow* (2007)

RB   *Letters to Robert Bloch and Others* (2015)

RK   *Letters to Rheinhart Kleiner and Others* (2010)

SL   *Selected Letters* (5 vols.; 1965–76)

CAS Clark Ashton Smith   HPL   H. P. Lovecraft   RHB R. H. Barlow
ET   Elizabeth Toldridge   JFM   James F. Morton

AMS autograph manuscript
JHL   John Hay Library, Brown University, Providence, R.I.
OED   *Oxford English Dictionary*
TMS   typescript
WT   *Weird Tales*

Note: Editorial ellipses are noted in brackets [. . .] *only* in Lovecraft's letters, since Lovecraft often used ellipses of three or more dots as punctuation. Ellipses in fiction, nonfiction, and poetry are always editorial.

Commentary

Dim Essences:
The Origins of
Fungi from Yuggoth

I.

You haunt the lonely strand where herons hide,
    And palm-framed sunsets open gates of flame;
Where marble moonbeams bridge the lapping tide
    To westward shores of dream without a name.

Here, in a haze of half-remembering,
    You catch faint sounds from that far, fabled beach.
The world is changed—your task henceforth to sing
    Dim, beckoning wonders you could never reach.[1]

H. P. Lovecraft's place in American letters is firmly established by the small body of his unique tales of fantasy and horror. It may surprise some that when Lovecraft was in his twenties he considered himself primarily to be a poet. Few realize that he wrote poetry (admittedly with widely disparate frequency) for forty of his forty-six years, or that his collected verse fills a very large volume. Yet Lovecraft would be forgotten had he written nothing more than the hundreds of his early poems.

Most of Lovecraft's verse was the product of his early days in amateur journalism. It is characterized by slavish imitation of a style not generally used since the middle eighteenth century, which modern readers find dull but which he admired and considered to be his poetic strength. He acknowledged readily that his verse had long been imitative:

---

1. "To a Young Poet in Dunedin" (May 1931), *AT* 191.

In my metrical novitiate I was, alas, a chronic & inveterate mimic; allowing my antiquarian tendencies to get the better of my abstract poetic feeling. As a result, the whole purpose of my writing soon became distorted—till at length I wrote only as a means of re-creating around me the atmosphere of my 18th century favourites. Self-expression as such sank out of sight, & my sole test of excellence was the degree with which I approached the style of Mr. Pope, Dr. Young, Mr. Thomson, Mr. Addison, Mr. Tickell, Mr. Parnell, Dr. Goldsmith, Dr. Johnson, & so on. My verse lost every vestige of originality & sincerity, its only care being to reproduce the typical forms & sentiments of the Georgian scene amidst which it was supposed to be produced. Language, vocabulary, ideas, imagery—everything succumbed to my one intense purpose of thinking & dreaming myself back into that world of periwigs & long ʃ's which for some odd reason seemed to me the normal world. Thus was formed a habit of imitativeness which I can never wholly shake off. Even when I break away, it is generally only through imitating something else![2]

Lovecraft very early on recognized this essential characteristic of his versifying. His poem "A Mississippi Autumn" was published in *Ole Miss* in December 1915 as by "Howard Phillips Lovecraft, Metrical Mechanic." He knew his verse had perfect rhyme and meter but often little more. When associates requested poems to order (or even when Lovecraft merely felt inclined to versify), he flipped on the switch and produced a poem, as when he boasted of composing "On Receiving a Picture of Swans" in ten minutes.[3] And so in taking stock late in life when R. H. Barlow expressed interest in gathering some of Lovecraft's early poetry into a book, he had the following to say:

During a long lifetime I've written reams on reams of general versified tripe—now heaped up or scattered beyond recall [. . .] The hundreds of other specimens—now largely beyond recall in dozens of forgotten amateur papers—are even worse than these. I wrote bushels in my day—nature verse, satire, parody, political & patriotic verse, general light verse, &c. &c. &c.—all of which I'd pay blackmail to keep out of sight today.[4]

Much of Lovecraft's early verse was written in heroic (or rocking horse)

---

2. HPL to ET, 8 March 1929, *ET* 37–38.
3. HPL to Rheinhart Kleiner, 14 September 1915, *RK* 20.
4. HPL to RHB, 13 June 1936, *OFF* 342. All his verse is gathered in *AT*.

couplets, in the manner of Dryden and Pope. Although out of fashion in the twentieth century,[5] Lovecraft favored it because of the ease with which he could quickly toss off lines suited to any particular occasion:

> Through Mr. Daas, I learn that you would 'like to see me get away from the heroic couplet, and see what I could do in other forms'. I fear that it is quite beyond me thus to leave a form of expression on which I seized almost by instinct, and in which nearly all my rhythmical efforts are cast. As the strength of Antaeus depended on his contact with Mother Earth, so does any possible merit in my verses depend on their execution in this regular and time-honoured measure. Take the form away, and nothing remains. I have no real poetic ability, and all that saves my verse from utter worthlessness is the care which I bestow on its metrical construction.[6]

It was almost inevitable, then, that around 1920 Lovecraft adopted fiction as his chief mode of genuine self-expression and virtually ceased writing poetry; and that during the last year of his life he felt that fewer than two dozen of his more than three hundred poems were worthy of preservation. Lovecraft wrote few poems after 1920, but those few, especially those composed during a forty-day outburst in late 1929 and early 1930, are among his most personal, introspective, and original. Supreme among those later efforts is the sonnet sequence *Fungi from Yuggoth*.

II.

> Sonnets, it seems to me, are preëminently the medium for complete ideas—in short, for a poetry as nearly intellectual as poetry can be without ceasing to be poetry. There is something inherently reflective and analytical about the very form of the sonnet.[7]

The elements that shaped *Fungi from Yuggoth* accumulated over Lovecraft's lifetime, but the most significant impetus to the composition was gained little more than a year before the poem was begun in the form of three significant sources.

---

5. But consider Vladimir Nabokov's 999-line "Pale Fire" (1962), an outstanding example of a truly engaging modern poem written entirely in heroic couplets.

6. HPL to Maurice W. Moe, 8 December 1914, *MWM* 37.

7. HPL to Frank Belknap Long, Jr., 25 February 1924, *SL* 1.317.

In December 1926, Donald Wandrei (1908–1987), at the age of eighteen, wrote Lovecraft for the first time. Wandrei had been corresponding with Clark Ashton Smith (also a correspondent of Lovecraft) since 1924, their discussions focusing largely on poetry. When Wandrei wrote Lovecraft, it was to return to Lovecraft two manuscripts sub-lent to Wandrei by Smith. Lovecraft and Wandrei initially had a high-spirited correspondence, for they exchanged close to half the entire volume of their letters in the year 1927 alone. It was not long before Wandrei started sending his poetry to Lovecraft, and Lovecraft read with it enthusiasm. On one occasion he wrote to Wandrei:

> Your poems [. . .] came this morning, & I must hasten to congratulate you on the undoubtedly deep & authentic poetic spirit which animates all your verses. [. . . I]t's quite difficult to select single items to praise, so essentially homogeneous & organically unified is the whole collection.
>
> Here & there are technical immaturities—stiffly turned phrases & lines with essential prose rather than poetic content—but these are so insignificant beside the cypress-like beauty of the whole that one sees & mentions them only incidentally & casually.[8]

The sheaf of poems Wandrei had sent was in fact the manuscript for a book he hoped to have published, though oddly he professed at the time to have lost interest in poetry. His interest must have been rekindled, for by December 1927 he had written his *Sonnets of the Midnight Hours.* He submitted them to *Weird Tales,* and the magazine accepted twelve pieces, which it published monthly from May 1928 to January 1929. But before Wandrei's sonnets began to appear in *Weird Tales,* he published *Ecstasy and Other Poems,* his first book of poetry.

At precisely this time, Lovecraft received a letter from another poet, Elizabeth Toldridge (1861–1940), a woman nearly thirty years older than Lovecraft. Their paths had crossed four years previous. In 1924, Lovecraft was asked to judge a poetry contest for the League of American Penwomen, and Toldridge's poem "In the Woods" was among the entries. In his response to Toldridge's query, Lovecraft wrote: "My memories of the entries in the contest are very indistinct, but I remember that I liked 'In the Woods' & spoke of it at some length. It is certainly very gratifying to know that you found my

---

8. HPL to Donald Wandrei, Monday [postmarked 3 February 1927], *DW* 40.

remarks encouraging, & I regret that my report was mislaid before you could re-read it." Because Toldridge had mislaid Lovecraft's report, she presumably had written him to see if he could pass along his comments to her once again, but of course he had no copy. He wrote: "If my opinion regarding your work will be of any value & encouragement to you, I shall be very glad to look over any verses you may wish to send, & give them such comment as might prove helpful. In these latter years I have done more with prose than with verse [. . .] but I still fancy I know an iambus from an anapaest, & a true poetic image from a pompous rhetorical vacuum."[9] And so began a voluminous and steady correspondence that lasted eight and a half years.

Over the years, Lovecraft received more than 200 poems from Toldridge, many of which he commented on, and most of which survive among his papers. His letters to her contain much the same advice that one finds in his "Department of Public Criticism" and similar essays, in which he pointed out faulty rhymes, limping meters, and trite images in the poetry of various amateur journalists. But somewhat unexpectedly, his advice to her is much less schoolmarmish than his typical criticisms of a decade before. He acknowledged: "At the time [of the poetry contest], I might have been more prone to side with the technical sticklers; but latterly I have been paying less & less attention to form, & more & more to imaginative content— so much so that my published criticisms in the old magazines of the United Amateur Press Association now strike me as somewhat absurd & pedantic."[10] One wonders if Lovecraft's awareness of his old criticisms, founded in technical exactness rather than "imaginative content," caused him to write less and less poetry over the years. Indeed, in 1928 he wrote but a single poem.

As their correspondence progressed, Lovecraft told Toldridge that he felt her poems "deserve preservation in book form if you could ever arrange for such a thing."[11] Roughly a year later, in September 1929, Toldridge told Lovecraft she had made a selection of her poems for a book that she titled *Winnings*. By mid-December, she had had a typescript of the book prepared.

9. HPL to ET, 16 October 1928, *ET* 15, 16.
10. HPL to ET, 16 October 1928, *ET* 15.
11. HPL to ET, 20 November 1928, *ET* 17.

It does not seem she pursued publication, for she merely left the manuscript in the care of Alfred A. Knopf and *Winnings* was never published.

Following the completion of "The Dunwich Horror" in the summer of 1928, Lovecraft wrote no more stories until 1930, when he began "The Whisperer in Darkness" on 24 February 1930. During that fallow period for fiction, his time was spent primarily at freelance editing and ghostwriting. As we have seen, his correspondence with two poets during that time focused heavily on poetry. Among the client work he was doing was assisting a longtime fellow amateur with a nonfiction book—about poetry. In November 1928, he wrote Toldridge: "A friend of mine in Wisconsin has written a book which I would like to recommend [. . .] but alas! it is not quite finished, although accepted (from a survey of the uncompleted MS.) by the Macmillan Co. This will be 'The Gateway to Poetry' by Maurice Winter Moe."[12] Moe (1882–1940), one of Lovecraft's earliest friends in amateur journalism and a correspondent of long standing, was a high school teacher in Milwaukee. *Doorways to Poetry* was a "poetical handbook—a treatise on the appreciation of poetry."[13] Moe had asked Lovecraft to examine the manuscript with an eye toward possible revision, and Lovecraft accepted, saying he would decline payment for "giving it the once-over."[14] His task, he said, would be merely to "supply examples of certain metrical forms & give advice & comment on certain exercises."[15]

Lovecraft described Moe's manuscript as "magnificent" and claimed it needed little editing on his part, but he confided to one correspondent that, despite its excellence, "the job does take time, confound it!"[16] Surely Lovecraft did not merely give the book the "once-over," for he did not complete work on it until September 1929.[17] Despite Macmillan's initial interest in *Doorways to Poetry*, it did not publish the book. As late as 1934, Lovecraft

12. HPL to ET, 20 November 1928, *ET* 21. This is HPL's only mention of the "Gateway[s] . . ." rather than "Doorways." At the time, Moe had been assisting Sterling Leonard and Harold Y. Moffett in preparing *Junior Literature: Book Two* (1930), published by Macmillan.

13. HPL to ET, 31 July 1929, *ET* 91.

14. HPL to Maurice W. Moe, January 1929, *MWM* 198.

15. HPL to August Derleth, 29 July 1929 , *ES* 1.203.

16. HPL to JFM, 30 July 1929, *JFM* 174.

17. HPL to ET, 1 October 1929, *ET* 109.

remained hopeful that the book may be published:

> But I wish some publisher had the nerve to issue Moe's own textbook— "Doorways to Poetry." I helped whip the MS. of this into shape, & can trut[h]fully & confidently say that I never saw a finer & clearer presentation of the rules, details, & basic principles of versification & poetic depiction. Moe has a notable gift for definition & illustration, & his treatise is so lucid & ample that almost anybody with even half a brain could slough off his major crudities after a close & repeated study of it. No one can equal Moe in anticipating all the typical weaknesses & difficulties of the imperfect bard— a result, no doubt, of long & observant years in amateurdom & in pedagogy.[18]

The publishers Holt and the Kenyon Press of Wauwatosa, Wis.,[19] also expressed interest, but in the end the book never appeared.[20] Lovecraft's investment of time and effort in *Doorways to Poetry* was not entirely without benefit, for the experience renewed his interest in the writing of poetry, poetry leaning more toward genuine self-expression.

While working on the book, Lovecraft composed a letter to Moe dated 25 July 1929 in 212 lines of heroic couplets that began prophetically: "Thanks for the gift, nor blame me if I TETER / And slip into mine antient vice of metre."[21] Not long after, Lovecraft was composing "specimen bits of verse for illustrative use in the body of the text—unusual metres, stanzaic forms, [and also] Italian & Shakespearian sonnets" to illustrate the differences between the two forms.[22]

In November Lovecraft slipped further into his "antient vice." He wrote to a correspondent "some malign influence—prob'ly revising that Moe text book on poetick appreciation—has got me invadin' one of Klarkash-Ton's provinces & relapsin' back into my antient weakness of attempted prosody."[23]

---

18. HPL to Edward H. Cole, 31 January 1934 (*AG* 71).

19. Moe's *Imagery Aids,* another poetry handbook, was published by the Kenyon Press in 1931.

20. RHB even planned to publish it in *Leaves.* One wonders, then, just how long it was.

21. "An Epistle to the Rt. Honble Maurice Winter Moe, Esq. of Zythopolis, in the Northwest Territory of HIS MAJESTY'S American Dominions" as by "L. Theobald, Jun." [Arkham House transcripts]; cf. *JFM* 175. *Teter,* a pun on the word *teeter,* referred to George E. *Teter,* a colleague of Moe and author of *An Introduction to Some Elements of Poetry,* a book HPL owned.

22. HPL to Donald Wandrei, 12 September 1929, *DW* 233.

23. HPL to JFM, [30 November] 1929, *JFM* 199. "Klarkash-Ton" refers to the California poet,

One product of Lovecraft's relapse was the 34-line send-up, "Lines upon the Magnates of the Pulp." It was, of course, not publishable by *Weird Tales,* and like his "letter" to Moe, it was in heroic couplets and basically for his own amusement. But then he wrote a 52-line poem in rhyming quatrains titled "The Outpost," about "a great King who fears to dream." In mid-November Lovecraft captured a "recent dream tableau" in "a sort of irregular semi-sonnet" that he named "Recapture."[24] He quickly followed "Recapture" with "The Ancient Track," a fairly long poem written in tetrameter couplets. Lovecraft submitted the three poems to *Weird Tales,* which bought "Recapture" and "The Ancient Track" for $14.50 but rejected "The Outpost" as being too long.[25] The poems of this period rank among Lovecraft's best because they were everything his early poems were not.

Lovecraft's correspondence with Donald Wandrei and Elizabeth Toldridge made for frequent, sometimes lengthy and detailed, discussion of poetry and of the poets' planned books. The overlapping of those discussions with the labor of editing, and writing illustrative material for, Moe's *Doorways to Poetry* surely aroused in Lovecraft a desire to versify once again, but now with an ear keener for natural expression. Still one more incident served to elicit more poetry from Lovecraft's pen. In November, he became engaged in a written discussion of weird fiction with the literary editor of the *Providence Journal,* Bertrand K. Hart (1892–1941). Hart's column, "The Sideshow," had begun to appear earlier that year and had become a favorite of Lovecraft. When Hart once wrote in his column about the mysterious disappearances of several trains, Lovecraft wrote Hart on the subject and the subsequent exchange of letters eventually turned to "the most eery story ever written."[26] Hart published in "The Sideshow" Lovecraft's general observations on weird fiction and now-famous list of favorite stories.

---

writer, painter, and sculptor Clark Ashton Smith (1893–1961), whose work HPL greatly admired. HPL paved the way for CAS's verse to appear in *WT* when in 1923 he encouraged the editor to break his policy not to publish poetry.

24. HPL to CAS, 19 November 1929, *Dreams and Fancies* 28; to ET, 26 November 1929, *ET* 116.

25. HPL to JFM, Freyr's Day, [6] December 1929, *JFM* 205. "The Ancient Track" is only eight lines shorter than "The Outpost." "The Outpost" was rejected presumably because it could not fit on a single printed page.

26. "The Sideshow" in the *Providence Journal,* 23 November 1929. Kenneth W. Faig, Jr., describes

Dim Essences

Around that time, Hart stumbled upon a recent collection of weird stories called *Beware After Dark!*, edited by T. Everett Harré. He was surprised to find that his own former residence at 7 Thomas Street in Providence had served as the setting of a scene in the story "The Call of Cthulhu," written three years before, and that its author was none other than H. P. Lovecraft. In "The Sideshow" for Friday, 29 November 1929, Hart wrote: "Personally I congratulate him upon the dark spirits he has evoked in Thomas Street, but I shall not be happy until, joining league with wraiths and ghouls, I have plumped down at least one large and abiding ghost by way of reprisal upon his own doorstep in Barnes Street. I think I shall teach it to moan in a minor dissonance every morning at three o'clock sharp with a clanking of chains."[27] In response to Hart's mock threat, Lovecraft wrote a sonnet, dedicated to Hart, describing a call from the ghost. "The Messenger" appeared in "The Sideshow" the following Tuesday.

But that was not all. On 7 December Lovecraft wrote a 48-line poem lamenting the demolition of the old brick warehouses along South Water Street. W. Chesley Worthington, editor of the column "These Plantations" that appeared Wednesdays in the *Providence Journal*,[28] urged readers to submit contributions of local interest. Lovecraft obliged with "The East India Brick Row" the very day he composed it. The experience of writing poetry again must have been exhilarating for Lovecraft. Most of his new attempts eschewed the heroic couplets he had favored more than a decade ago, and poetry in various forms was showing itself a suitable medium for expression of his thoughts and emotions. Lovecraft previously had few sales of his poetry—*Weird Tales,* and perhaps the *National Enquirer* and *National Magazine*—but professional publications were now buying his verses.

Then, in mid-December, Lovecraft commenced the writing of *Fungi from Yuggoth.* As in the case of many of Lovecraft's great writings, the poem came to be because of a number of felicitous coincidences, such as those noted above. Yet another significant influence on *Fungi from Yuggoth* was Lovecraft's frequent and lengthy discussions of his past, with particular

the exchange between HPL and Hart in his essay, "HPL's Own Book of Weird Fiction."

27. *The Sideshow of B. K. Hart* 48.

28. HPL to W. Chesley Worthington, 7 December 1929 (ms., Providence Athenaeum).

reflection on his childhood days, as found throughout his letters of 1929. A letter to August Derleth from late December 1929—written just before he wrote *Fungi from Yuggoth*—is typical of those discussions:

> The idea of impersonal pageantry & time-&-space-defying phantasy has always—quite literally from the very dawn of consciousness—been so inextricably bound up with my inmost thought & feeling, that any searching transcript of my moods would sound highly artificial, exotic, & flavoured with conventional images, no matter how utterly faithful it might be in truth. What has haunted my dreams for nearly forty years is *a strange sense of adventurous expectancy connected with landscape & architecture & sky-effects.* I can see myself as a child of 2½ on the railway bridge at Auburndale, Mass., looking across & downward at the business part of the town, & feeling the imminence of some wonder which I could neither describe nor fully conceive—& there has never been a subsequent hour of my life when kindred sensations have been absent. I wish I could get the idea on paper—the sense of marvel & liberation hiding in obscure dimensions & problematically reachable at rare instants through vistas of ancient streets, across leagues of strange hill country, or up endless flights of marble steps culminating in tiers of balustraded terraces. Odd stuff—& needing a greater poet than I for effective aesthetic utilisation.[29]

Many other immediate influences impinged on the composition of

29. HPL to August Derleth, Sunday [15 December 1929], *ES* 1.237–38. Note that HPL says a *poet* is needed to express his ideas, a role he himself served a few weeks later.

Fungi from Yuggoth. R. H. Barlow, in his "[Memories of Lovecraft (1934)]," observed that "Azathoth—Nyarlathotep was based on a dream-name, as was also the first and others of the *Fungi from Yuggoth,*"[30] and the night-gaunts of Lovecraft's childhood nightmares also were employed. It is evident that Lovecraft browsed through his commonplace book during composition of the poem. In 1934, when he presented the notebook to Barlow, he acknowledged that five entries inspired certain sonnets, but the influence of other entries can clearly be seen. The death of Everett McNeil of the Kalem Club in mid-December 1929 inspired "The Pigeon-Flyers" and perhaps "The Courtyard." Scenes and themes from stories that had appeared in *Weird Tales,* some of Lovecraft's own stories such as "Celephaïs" and *The Dream-Quest of Unknown Kadath,* and assorted personal recollections also found their way into the poem.

Barlow, whom Lovecraft appointed his literary executor, has written that the manuscript of *Fungi from Yuggoth* "consists of an interesting set of draughts which would lend themselves well to facsimile reproduction some day."[31] They do indeed, for they illustrate the painstaking labor that went into the poem's composition. Each leaf of the twenty-page manuscript is blanketed with false starts, deletions, heavy interlining of insertions, and extensive rewriting. On the first page of the manuscript, Lovecraft proclaimed "Dec. 27, 1929" and "14 sonnets 196 lines." On page 8 he wrote, "16 additional sonnets—Dec. 28, 1929–Jany 2, 1930" and "Total to Jany 2—30 sonnets = 420 lines $105 at W.T. rates." (The original draft of 490 lines would have earned Lovecraft $122.50 could he have sold the entire poem.) In other words, it seems he drafted or at least sketched out not quite half the poem in one day, assuming he began the poem on 27 December. Over the next six days he composed sixteen more sonnets.[32] Page 11 of the manuscript contains at the bottom a cluster of thirty-five brief notes—ideas Lovecraft did not want to lose in the heat of composition so that they could be developed later, and he did indeed develop several of those notes into poems (see Appendix A). There is a note on page 8 "copy on p. 5—first set of sheets" and another on page 9 that reads "Begin p. 6." These notes coincide with

30. *OFF* 404. The piece contains notes RHB had made of topics discussed in person with HPL.

31. RHB, "The Wind That Is in the Grass," *OFF* xxxii.

32. HPL may well have spent some time after 2 January revising and refining the poem.

the placement of "Antarktos" (page 8) on page 5 of the typescript that he eventually made, and "The Window" (page 9) on page 6. "Harbour Whistles" (p. 19) bears the date "Jany 3, 1930," but presumably that pertains to the previous two sonnets as well. Page 20 contains two sonnets, with the date "Jany 4, 1930" next to "Evening Star."

After a long period of poetic dormancy, Lovecraft wrote forty poems in a forty-day period. While working on *Fungi from Yuggoth*, he mockingly complained: "I had sworn to cut out rhyming—but that bird [Moe] got me doing jingles for metrically illustrative purposes, and now—confound it—I can't stop!"[33] As it was, he probably wrote no more than ten more poems before his death in 1937. Lovecraft soon typed a clean copy of the poem, but when he did so, he did not include "Evening Star" and "Continuity" (numbered XXXIV and XXXV in the draft). Since he told correspondents he might compose still more sonnets for *Fungi from Yuggoth*, he kept those two poems aside, so that they could in time take their proper place at the very end of the sequence and be numbered accordingly.

"The East India Brick Row" appeared in "These Plantations" on 8 January 1930. Lovecraft wrote a note of thanks to the editor on 10 January for his copy of the published poem, adding, "I am very grateful for the space spared for my effusion, & hope that it did not cause you any really nerve-racking problem of format. The neat, symmetrical location of the piece is highly pleasing."[34] His success at landing "The East India Brick Row" inspired him to submit *Fungi from Yuggoth* for consideration. Lovecraft sent the entire typescript of the poem to the *Journal* for perusal, and the paper selected five poems. One can only imagine what Worthington and his readers made of "night-gaunts" and "puffed shoggoths [that] splash in doubtful sleep."

Inevitably, Lovecraft began circulating *Fungi from Yuggoth* among colleagues for them to read. In January 1930, he wrote to August Derleth:

> As for the sonnet you dislike—#10—I've had my doubts about that, too, because its appreciation depends upon a familiarity with the actual customs of the "Hell's Kitchen" slum in New York, where bonfire-building & pigeon-flying are the two leading recreations of youth. To one unacquainted with

33. HPL to JFM, The Ides of Martinus [12 March 1930], *JFM* 224.

34. HPL to W. Chesley Worthington, 10 January 1930 (ms., Providence Athenaeum).

the region & its *mores*, the sonnet would inevitably have a tendency to seem pointless. That ought to give it an excellent chance with Wright, judging from the majority of the "poems" he uses. I've ground out about 20 more of these things, & shall see what Brother Farnsworth has to say of them.[35]

Lovecraft's letters to various individuals at the time seem to give conflicting information about the content of the poem. On 17 January 1930, he wrote to Clark Ashton Smith: "I have crystallised my latest set of bizarre moods in a series of some 35 sonnets called 'Fungi from Yuggoth'—which I'll shew you when Wright sends them back, as he undoubtedly will."[36] But Lovecraft repeatedly told correspondents that the poem had *thirty-three* sonnets, as when a letter accompanied the typescript. There are no references to thirty-five around this time save in his letter to Smith, written before the sonnets had been typed. For instance, in a letter to Elizabeth Toldridge from late January 1930, Lovecraft wrote "Incidentally—my 'Fungi' have just come back, & I am enclosing them herewith. There are 33 here, but I shall probably grind out a dozen or so more before I consider the sequence concluded."[37] He held that thought for years. In advising a young writer years later, Lovecraft wrote: "Wait till the ideas spontaneously come. That's the way I always do. I wrote 35 'Fungi from Yuggoth' in 1929–30, & haven't written any since!"[38] So in other words, Lovecraft informed Smith that he had in fact *written* thirty-five poems, as evidenced by the draft manuscript. But as noted, he put XXXIV and XXXV aside in the event he might write "grind out" more poems. For years, the typescript Lovecraft circulated among correspondents and publishers consisted of only thirty-three poems. In a letter to August Derleth, written when he was up to only the fourth page of his new story "The Whisperer in Darkness" (i.e., sometime shortly after 24 February 1930), Lovecraft wrote: "Of the 33 'Fungi from Yuggoth' which I wrote & sent around, Wright has taken 10, & the

---

35. *ES* 1.242. By the time HPL had written Derleth, it seems he would have written far more than merely roughly twenty poems. It is unlikely that he would have sent Derleth but a single poem, so the reference to only "The Pigeon-Flyers" is unclear.

36. HPL to CAS, *DS* 198–99.

37. HPL to ET, late January 1930, *ET* 124. "Herewith" refers to his typescript only. He had not yet typed the two closing sonnets, pending possible composition of others.

38. HPL to Duane W. Rimel, 12 September 1934, *FLB* 215.

Providence Journal five more."[39]

Once the heat of composition had ebbed, Lovecraft could then tell his correspondents what he had hoped to achieve in the poem. To Clark Ashton Smith, he wrote:

> here are my Yuggothian Fungi, to be returned at leisure. Nothing notable about them—but they at least embody certain moods & images. Some of the themes are really more adapted to fiction—so that I shall probably make stories of them whenever I get that constantly-deferred creative opportunity I am always waiting for. You will see something of my scenic or landscape-architectural tendency in these verses—especially suggestions of unplaceable or half-forgotten scenes. These vague, elusive pseudo-memories have haunted me ever since I was an infant, & are quite a typical ingredient of my psychology & aesthetic attitude.[40]

Lovecraft wrote at length to James F. Morton of his notion of adventurous expectancy, including with his letter *Fungi from Yuggoth* to illustrate what he meant by it. He identified sonnets V, XIII, XIV, XVIII, XIX, XXIII, XXVIII, XXX, and XXXIII as "items which illustrate my moods & indicate why no mapped out programme could ever be of any value to me."[41] "Continuity" is conspicuously absent from the list of especially personal poems, but again, Lovecraft did not feel that the entire sonnet sequence was yet concretized, and so it was not yet part of the typescript. As late as 20 July 1930, he sent his only typed copy of the poem to Robert E. Howard, saying in the accompanying letter: "'The Dweller' is one of a long series of weird metrical attempts in something like the sonnet form—& since you express a wish to see more, I am enclosing a ms. which contains some thirty-three."[42]

Lovecraft acknowledged the profundity of *Fungi from Yuggoth* when he wrote at the conclusion of a lengthy letter to a friend: "I'm afraid that all this

---

39. HPL to August Derleth, Monday [3 March 1930], *ES* 1.250.

40. HPL to CAS, 2 February 1930, *DS* 204. CAS obtained a personal copy of the poem in September 1934.

41. HPL to JFM, The Ides of Martinus [12 March 1930], *JFM* 224. It is telling that the poem's most "unplaceable or half-forgotten scenes" contain no overt suggestion of horror (as do "Zaman's Hill," "The Courtyard," "Night-Gaunts," "Nyarlathotep," "Azathoth," and "St. Toad's").

42. HPL to Robert E. Howard, 20 July 1930, *MF* 1.24. HPL may have sent Howard only a clipping of "The Dweller" initially, inspiring Howard to ask to see more such verse.

prose doesn't tell half so much about the old man as certain of his quasi-sonneteering *Fungi from Yuggoth.*"[43] It is unfortunate that those who published the poems tended to pass over the most reflective sonnets. Indeed, a key poem, "Expectancy," was never published in Lovecraft's lifetime.

III.

In my actual imaginative contact with life, I am vastly more responsive to beauty than to horror.[44]

Winfield Townley Scott has suggested that Edwin Arlington Robinson's *Sonnets, 1889–1927* (1928) exerted a strong influence on the modern tone of Lovecraft's poetry of the mid-1920s and onward, but there is no evidence to suggest this.[45] Lovecraft's letters, published and unpublished, contain scant reference to Robinson—I find only one—which is unusual if Robinson were the profound influence Scott believed him to be. Consider Lovecraft's effusive comments over the years about Dunsany, Poe, Machen, Blackwood, and other writers. But Lovecraft did recognize Robinson as one of the leading poets of the day.[46] As noted, Lovecraft had been

43. HPL to Maurice W. Moe, 5 April 1931, *MWM* 304.

44. HPL to ET, 8 March 1929, *ET* 39.

45. See "A Parenthesis on Lovecraft as Poet": "I am inclined to think, with nothing to go on but internal evidence, that Lovecraft had been reading Edwin Arlington Robinson. In his 'A Year Off' the phrase 'shame the sages' certainly echoes Robinson's line, 'Bereft enough to shame a sage,' in 'The Poor Relation.' And the phrasing, the tone, the general approach of the 'Fungi' sonnets are repeatedly Robinsonian" (Cannon, *Lovecraft Remembered* 434). Edmund Wilson repeats this idea in "Tales of the Marvellous and the Ridiculous" (Joshi, *Four Decades* 48), but he merely echoes Scott, whose essay he read in *Marginalia*, a book on which he was commenting in his essay. HPL wrote "A Year Off" in 1925, three years before the publication of Robinson's *Sonnets*. Robinson's poem appeared as "Pauvrette" in the *Outlook* (30 June 1915): 504–5, and as "The Poor Relation" in *The Man against the Sky* (1916) 45–47. Even so, it is unlikely that HPL read the poem or that he read much of Robinson. More likely, both HPL and Robinson independently derived the phrase from an as yet unidentified common source that seems to derive from 1 Cor. 1:27 or a similar passage: "God chose the foolish things of the world to shame the wise [i.e., sages]; God chose the weak things of the world to shame the strong."

46. While working with Moe on *Doorways to Poetry*, HPL made the following suggestion to Moe regarding the book: "A few parallel passages—arrang'd in your inimitable manner—would hale a helluva lot to get the idee across in quick, nifty fashion. You might line up a bird like William Morris beside a modern egg like Bob Frost—Matt Arnold beside Ed Robinson—Alf

SONNETS of the MIDNIGHT·HOURS
BY DONALD WANDREI

rethinking his previous poetic tendencies and changing them all on his own. Some say that the work of Clark Ashton Smith influenced Lovecraft's later poetry, but that is not likely, or at best, such influence is only slight. If anything, the two poets were kindred spirits who employed similar themes, but one would never mistake the work of one poet for that of the other. Clearly the single most significant stylistic influence of *Fungi from Yuggoth* was Donald Wandrei's *Sonnets of the Midnight Hours*.

Lovecraft read Wandrei's sonnets in the autumn of 1927 when Wandrei was only nineteen.[47] *Ecstasy and Other Poems,* Wandrei's first book of poetry, was published the following year by W. Paul Cook's Recluse Press. Wandrei intended to publish his sonnets in a volume titled *The Midnight Hours,* but that never came to be, although selections of the sonnets appeared in the Arkham House anthology *Dark of the Moon* (1947) and years later in his *Poems for Midnight* (1964). The sonnets do not form a clear narrative sequence, and Wandrei continually rewrote, reordered, and added to them. As the series title implies, the poems derived from Wandrei's dreams, much as *Fungi from Yuggoth* was influenced in large part by Lovecraft's own. Wandrei submitted his sonnets to *Weird Tales* around January 1928, and Farnsworth Wright accepted twelve of them. The poems appeared in eleven consecutive issues of *Weird Tales* from May 1928 to March 1929 under the heading "Sonnets of the Midnight Hours," with an illustrative headpiece

Tennyson or Henry Longfellow alongside of Jack Masefield or A. E. Housman, Al Swinburne over-against Conrad Aiken—yuh get what I mean" (27 July 1929, *MWM* 223).

47. HPL to Frank Belknap Long, Jr., November 1927, *SL* 2.186: "This reminds me to exclaim anent the excellence of Wandrei's recent poetry. The child is certainly making astonishing strides—as the *Sonnets of the Midnight Hours* shew in particular." The letter may be slightly misdated, for HPL seemed to have obtained the poems for reading c. 19 December.

by Hugh Rankin. They were numbered 1 through 12 to indicate that they were part of a unified group of poems, but the numbering was not Wandrei's (he himself did not number the poems) and the poems did not appear in a sequence duplicated in any later collection.[48] The selections from *Fungi from Yuggoth* appeared in *Weird Tales* in a similar format.

It was Wandrei who had advised Lovecraft to employ the sonnet form:

> In our discussions of poetry I often urged him to consider the sonnet as a worthy form for his impressions, moods, and vivid nightmares. The sonnet was a natural form for him, for it lent itself equally well to calm reason or deep emotion, pure imagery or abstract thought, compressed much in brief space, was ideally suited for short intervals of available writing time, and was not a difficult form to master. Whether from my urging or from some other stimulus, he did indeed write many fine sonnets in later years, called *Fungi from Yuggoth*.[49]

Lovecraft did indeed adopt, or, more precisely, *adapt* the form in his later work. He referred to his sonnets as "quasi-sonneteering," "pseudo-sonnets," "near sonnet[s]," and "a long series of weird metrical attempts in something like the sonnet form,"[50] rarely as "sonnets." He had described the earlier "Recapture" as an "irregular semi-sonnet," and each sonnet of *Fungi from Yuggoth* is very similar to it in construction. Lovecraft was not being excessively modest or self-deprecating (although there is an element of this in his comments, as in all his comments about his own work), seeming to

48. Of the sonnets that appeared in *WT*, only nine appeared in later printings of the sequence. The grouping published in *Dark of the Moon* comprises twenty poems, that in *Poems for Midnight* twenty-six. In the latter two printings, the poems are unnumbered, are ordered differently in both books, and in some cases differ significantly in wording. We can only be certain that HPL read the poems that appeared in *WT*, but he may well have read others in manuscript. Regarding the number of poems, Wandrei wrote to August Derleth (27 November 1945), presumably in preparing them for *Dark of the Moon:* "There were 26 in all, but unless some of them can be greatly improved, they will be reduced to 20 or 22. I have made revisions on all but 4 or 5" (in Joshi, "The Poetry of Donald Wandrei," *Sanctity and Sin* 16).

49. "Lovecraft in Providence" 134. Wandrei's urging HPL to write sonnets may have been in *personal* discussion during his visit with HPL in 1927, for there is no mention of this in their letters.

50. HPL to Maurice W. Moe, 5 April 1931, *MWM* 304; to Harry O. Fischer, late February 1937, *CLM* 323; to J. Vernon Shea, 8–22 November 1933 (*JVS* 192); and to Robert E. Howard, 20 July 1930, *MF* 24.

imply that the poems were inferior to *real* sonnets. But he simply was acknowledging that, technically speaking (as he so often did), the individual poems of *Fungi from Yuggoth* are, in fact, not actual sonnets. Just as Wandrei's *Sonnets of the Midnight Hours* exhibit some disregard for the strict requirements of the sonnet form, so too does *Fungi from Yuggoth*.

Sonnets typically follow either of two forms: the Italian or Petrarchan, and the English or Shakespearean. The Italian sonnet consists of two parts: the octave, whose rhyme scheme is *abbaabba,* and the sestet, usually *cdecde* or *cdcdcd.* Other rhyme patterns for the sestet, such as *cdedce, cdeced, ccdede, ccdccd,* or *ccdeed,* are allowable, although they are less common. A blank line usually separates the two parts visually. The essence of the form is the unequal relationship between the octave and the sestet in number of lines, rhyme pattern, and subject. Lines 1 to 4 state the subject, lines 5 to 8 prove it, lines 9 to 11 confirm it, and lines 12 to 14 draw the conclusion. The following poem by Lovecraft constitutes a true Italian sonnet:

> Sonnets are sighs, breathed beautiful and brief
> From spirits sobered by their weight of dreams;
> Figures in jade whose perfection gleams
> A tortured thought too luminous for grief,
> Shaped with that ecstasy which brings relief
> And rest, distilled from woe's encircling streams.
> Solemn and high the poet's chosen themes,
> Their stray tones gathered to a stately sheaf.
>
> Not mine to mould such Tuscan symphonies,
> Wherein each note must sound the singer's mood;
> Octave advance and sestet retrogress
> In subtler turns than common vision sees;
> Dulness stands lost in an enchanted wood
> Pathless to eyes untouched by loveliness.[51]

51. This poem and the one following survive as a mimeographed sheet, indicated only as "A" and "B" under the title "Sonnet Study," presumably provided by Moe. (The sheet contains one other sonnet by another poet.) The following note is Moe's: "This is the Italian sonnet. The octave (the first 8 lines) always has the a-b-b-a a-b-b-a rime-scheme, and is usually objective, drawing a picture or stating a fact. The sestet (last six lines) has any combination of c-d or c-d-e rimes and is

Strictly speaking, only I, IV, V, VIII, XIII, XVI, XX, XXVII, and XXIX of *Fungi from Yuggoth* might be considered to be of the Italian form—at least on the basis of the rhyme scheme. The rhyme schemes of their sestets, however, are rather uncommon and the themes do not show the tension between the octave and sestet demanded by the form. The poems are more nearly simple narratives told in verse.

The English sonnet consists of three quatrains written in open rhyme (*rima alterna*) and concludes with a couplet that has the effect of serving as an epigram or summary. The rhyme scheme typically is *ababcdcdefefgg*, with no breaks indicated between the four rhyme groupings. An alternative is the linked rhyme: *ababbcbccdcdee*. The proportions of the English sonnet are twelve to two, as opposed to eight to six in the Italian sonnet. The following is Lovecraft's example of a sonnet in the English form:

> The subtle mind in subtle tones can speak,
>   Nor trip in paths Italianate;
> Finding the door for which his wishes seek
>   In the slow sonnet which made Petrarch great.
>
> Such ordered shadings, drawn with grave intent,
>   A thousand charms of musing bring to light,
> As brooding dusk reveals in his descent
>   The countless day-enshrouded orbs of night.
>
> But we, of plainer, hardier metal wrought,
>   A straighter path demand, whose hedge and goal
> May suit the Saxon's undivided thought,
>   And guide his changeless impulse, warm and whole:
>
> Summing his message in one final shout
> That speaks his mind and drowns all wavering out.[52]

usually subjective, drawing a conclusion from what is said in the octave, though not invariably" (ms., JHL). The poems originate in HPL's letter to Moe of 25 July [1929] (found in the Arkham House transcripts of HPL's letters), where he labels sonnet A as "Dago Stuff," by "Al Capone (Cashen Carey's Tr.)" and B as "White Man Stuff by B. Jonson Flomont-Betcher." In the Arkham House transcript, neither poem has line breaks.

52. The following is also by Moe: "This sonnet is of the Elizabethan or Shakespearean type. Its

Lovecraft wrote seven sonnets of *Fungi from Yuggoth* in the form of the English sonnet, although he indicated a break between lines 8 and 9, as he did in all the other sonnets.

There are seven rhyme patterns in *Fungi from Yuggoth*, most being simply variations of the Italian and English forms:

Italian   *abbaabba cdcdee* I, IV, XVI
           abbaabba cddcee V, VIII, XIII, XX, XXVIII, XXIX

English[53] *ababcdcd efefgg* II, III, VI, VII, XV, XXII, XXIII
           abbacddc efefgg IX, XII, XVII, XIX, XXVII
           ababcddc effegg X
           abbacddc effegg XIV, XVIII, XXI, XXIV, XXV, XXVI, XXX,
                            XXXI, XXXII, XXXIII, XXXIV, XXXV, XXXVI
           abbacdcd efefgg XI

Lovecraft's effective use of the closing couplet in each sonnet is perhaps the poem's most striking quality, although the mixture of so many different rhyme patterns weakens the overall effect somewhat.

It is true that the sonnet form is not entirely rigid. Other poets have composed many variations on the form, perhaps most notably Gerard Manley Hopkins's highly compressed "curtal" sonnet, "Pied Beauty." But number of lines, rhyme pattern, and meter do not alone a sonnet make. Lovecraft knew and consciously disregarded the fundamental requirements of the classic sonnet, for he was merely writing very short stories in verse form or, as he said, "pseudo-sonnets."[54]

In *Fungi from Yuggoth* Lovecraft avoided the lofty language typical of the classic sonnet. He wrote to Elizabeth Toldridge: "You will notice throughout the series my effort to break away from tawdry & artificial 'poetic diction' & write in the living language of normal utterance. Probably I

three quatrains with alternate rimes (a-b-a-b c-d-c-d) usually state three different aspects of some thought, or develop it in three gradual steps, as in this example. The couplet rounds out the idea, often with an unexpected thought" (ms., JHL).

53. But note that HPL cast his "Elizabethan" sonnets in two stanzas, not four as in his example (possibly Moe's concoction), or even in only one as in the case of Shakespeare's own sonnets.

54. HPL to Duane W. Rimel, 13 April 1934 (*FLB* 169), in which he acknowledges that "The Yuggothian fungi vary in precise rhyme-scheme. Some are true sonnets, others are not."

haven't fully succeeded, but this junk at least implies a start in the right direction."[55] His advice to Toldridge about adjusting her poetry to "the contemporary scene" is a telling reflection on his own change from the archaic couplets of his early poetry to the distinctly modern *Fungi from Yuggoth*:

> The essential quality of poetic vision does not depend on period or perspective or theme; & after your view is re-focussed to the values & proportions now recognised as sound, you will find yourself reacting to them just as richly & naturally as you formerly reacted to the values & proportions of the preceding age. This does not involve any loss or impairment of personality or individual nature. The individual quality is not a matter of theme, but is simply the manner in which one responds to any theme that one does respond to. The history of poetry is full of cases of writers who have lived from one age into another & changed their styles accordingly. Byron, for instance, first wrote in the Georgian manner & then wholly recast himself in the mould of the romantic revival—as did many another poet who lived in the early XIX century. And in a later age, Amy Lowell discarded the late XIX century tradition for the imagistic thought of the early XX century. In neither case was the poet's essential personality changed. They merely continued to express in their own respective ways the impressions which impinged upon them. The change was not in them, but in the impinging impressions.[56]

When Lovecraft wrote these words, he had already cast aside the archaic poetic forms he had used ten to fifteen years earlier, allowing his personality to emerge in a new, fresh, more natural form. Part of that naturalness occurs through a general loosening of the metronomic sense of rhythm that Lovecraft had formerly employed. Donald R. Burleson perceives "scansion problems" in the poem "Mirage," consisting mostly of slightly elided or extended pronunciations of words in order to fit the line. (Such examples can be seen throughout the long poem.) But this practice is common and not at all to be frowned upon. After all, Lovecraft was striving to write "in the living language of normal utterance." Thus, it would be a mistake to attempt to force Lovecraft's lines into rigid iambic pentameter. Consider these examples:

55. HPL to ET, late January 1930, *ET* 124.
56. HPL to ET, late January 1930, *ET* 123.

˘ –	˘ –	˘ –	˘ –	˘ –	
There is	in cer-	tain an-	cient things	a trace	XXXVI.1
˘ –	– –	– ˘ ˘	– ˘	–	
The birds	fly out,	over an	ocean	waste	XXIX.2
– –	– –	˘ –	˘ –	˘ –	
False, phan-	tom tri-	fles of	some vast-	er plan	XXXII.12
– ˘ ˘	– ˘	– ˘	– ˘	–	
Echoes from	outer	voids, and	subtle	clues	XXXIII.11

The first, from "Continuity," is perfect iambic pentameter. The others are not, but nevertheless are not out of place. Of course, strict iambic pentameter is technically superior, but great skill is required to accomplish that. Lovecraft knowingly avoided formality, and was not above using an unnecessary modifier such as *half-* from time to time, surely to arouse uncertainty and unsettledness in the reader with such phrases as "half-lost," "half-animate," "half-limitless," and others, but also to conveniently fill a line with a needed syllable.

Consider Lovecraft's letter to Maurice Moe discussing prosody:

> [. . .] all these damn technical terms—feet, accents, metre, and what the hell—are simply academick devices to account for something already existing; something so vague, flexible, and irregular that it can never be captured in exact rules and names. As a result, schoolbook precepts and definitions are always incomplete, ambiguous, varied, and even conflicting. The irregular lines of a guy like old [Robert] Bridges—that is, a good part of 'em—*can be scanned in more than one way* according to how one interprets the foot-boundaries.[57]

And so it is with scansion in Lovecraft's poem.

Fungi from Yuggoth contains many ideas and opinions found in Lovecraft's early poetry, but here they are expressed more naturally and fluidity. While *Fungi from Yuggoth* may not be as technically perfect as his early poems, it has a vitality those early poems lacked, which can be attributed to his willingness to bend slightly the rules of prosody.

---

57. HPL to Maurice W. Moe 29 July 1934, *MWM* 352.

IV.

The modern bard reſtrains poetic rage,
To fit his couplets to a quarter-page. . . .
None heeds his worth; his liſtless lines are bought
Because some favour'd ſtory is too short.
No critic's sneer his honeſt ire incites,
For none, forsooth, peruses what he writes![58]

Fungi from Yuggoth was never published in its entirety in Lovecraft's lifetime. Although he would have been pleased to see the poem published as a whole, he was content to have the sonnets published individually. He wrote to a correspondent early on: "I am letting the Prov. Journal have a firſt chance at them, & what they return I shall send to *Weird Tales*. The residue after this will go to *Driftwind* [. . .] & what they don't want I shall dump on the amateur press."[59] An informal log Lovecraft kept on the autograph manuscript of the poem shows that he followed that plan (see Table 1). Although he had calculated the potential earnings of the poem by sale of the whole at *Weird Tales* rates, he did indeed send it firſt to the *Providence Journal*. Apparently Lovecraft circulated his typescript of the poem to proſpeſtive publishers, who then selected individual items for publication. The *Journal* paid \$17.50 for the five poems it published in the literary seſtion of the Wednesday edition between 12 March and 14 May 1930.

Table 1

Notes on page 1 of the manuscript of *Fungi from Yuggoth* (35 sonnets).

Journal	XI, XX, XXIX, XXX, XXXI
possibly*	XIV, XVI, XXVI
WT	IX, XIII, XIV, XV, XIX, XXI, XXII, XXIII, XXVII, XXXII
Driftwind	VI, VIII, XVI, XXVI
Recluse	I, II, III, VII, XII, XVIII
Silver Fern	XXXIII

*"Possibly" means that the poems might be submitted to or accepted by the *Providence Journal* or another periodical. Later, Lovecraft encircled "XIV" and wrote "WT" next to it, for XIV is listed under *WT* below. Lovecraft submitted only I–III to the *Recluse,* but they never appeared there. See also Table 2.

---

58. "The Magazine Poet" (1915), *AT* 225–26.1–2, 11–14.
59. HPL to ET, [11 February 1930], *ET* 127.

Weird Tales selected only 10 sonnets. Lovecraft submitted a separate transcript of those poems, stating: "here are your 10 hand-picked Fungi—and may they adorn with appropriate morbidity the unhallowed gardens which bloom betwixt your covers! Trust I've copied them correctly, and hope the typothetae Corneliarum will do likewise."[60] They appeared in seven consecutive issues of *Weird Tales* between September 1930 and April 1931 and were numbered 1 through 10 to show they were thematically related, similar to what was done with Donald Wandrei's *Sonnets of the Midnight Hours*.[61] Lovecraft's own ordering and numbering of the poems were not followed. The poems appeared under the title "Fungi from Yuggoth" with a headpiece by Hugh Rankin, again similar to that for Wandrei's *Sonnets*, apparently depicting scenes from "Nyarlathotep," "Night-Gaunts" [not published in *Weird Tales*], and "The Courtyard." For these, Lovecraft earned $35, for a total sales to *Weird Tales* and the *Journal* of $52.50. He never attempted to place other parts of *Fungi from Yuggoth* with *Weird Tales*, but in the end the magazine published most of the poems after his death, at the behest of August Derleth.

Other poems appeared in amateur venues. Lovecraft stated that he submitted the remainder of *Fungi from Yuggoth* to Walter J. Coates of *Driftwind*, who took "The Lamp," "The Port," "The Window," and "The Familiars." "Harbour Whistles" was taken by both *L'Alouette*, edited by Charles A. A. Parker of Medford, Mass., and *Silver Fern*, by Robert G. Barr of Christchurch, New Zealand. Lovecraft earmarked "The Book," "Pursuit," "The Key," "Zaman's Hill," "The Howler," and "The Gardens of Yin" for the second issue of W. Paul Cook's *Recluse*, but in the end provided only the first three.[62] Cook typeset about 100 pages, or half the issue, and even printed 40 pages. Lovecraft had read proofs of his story "The Strange High House in the Mist" for the same issue. However, the death

60. HPL to Farnsworth Wright, c. January 1930 (*Lovecraft Annual* 8 [2014]: 21). HPL refers to "the typesetters of Cornelius" (i.e, George M., George H., and P. W. Cornelius), who owned the company that printed *WT* and the magazine's major creditor when it was in financial straits.

61. Two poems appeared each in the issues for September 1930, January 1931, and February–March 1931. As noted, the entire sequence (thirty-five poems) would have earned HPL $122.50 had it been accepted, a rather high price to pay for "filler." HPL was paid $165 for "The Call of Cthulhu" (*WT*, February 1928).

62. See pp. 249–50 regarding the typescript submitted to Cook.

FUNGI·from·YUGGOTH
By H.P. LOVECRAFT

of Cook's wife interfered with completion of the magazine.

Lovecraft transferred most of his informal submittal log from the draft manuscript to his typescript of the poem (see Table 2). He had recorded acceptances on his draft of the poem for his own edification, but later wrote notes of acceptance on the typescript to indicate to prospective publishers which poems had already been spoken for. Since the poems for the *Recluse* and one for *Ripples from Lake Champlain* (earmarked on the draft) were not used, they became free for consideration. Over the years, the typescript was circulated among other prospective amateur publishers who selected poems from those yet unpublished. Most publishers of the individual poems did not acknowledge that they were part of a longer work.

In 1931, Lovecraft sent the poem once again to *Driftwind*, which now selected "Recognition," "The Howler," "The Window," "The Gardens of Yin," and "The Canal."[63] "The Canal" was later published in an anthology edited by Coates titled *Harvest: A Sheaf of Poems from* Driftwind.[64] Earl Clifford Kelley, president of the National Amateur Press Association, selected "The Pigeon-Flyers" and "A Memory" for *Ripples from Lake Champlain,* but only "The Pigeon-Flyers" was published because Kelley had committed suicide in July 1932, before "A Memory" could be published.[65] In

---

63. "The Book," which appeared in *Driftwind* for April 1937, was the tenth sonnet to appear in that magazine, but it probably was not submitted by HPL. *Driftwind* acknowledged its previous appearance in *Fantasy Fan.*

64. *Harvest* was printed in an edition of 225 copies, of which 75 were bound in boards. HPL had claimed this was the only appearance of his poetry between hard covers, although *The Poetical Works of Jonathan E. Hoag* (1923) contains seven of his poems. He likely dismissed this publication because he himself had edited the book, which was privately published.

65. See HPL to RHB, [22 August 1934], *OFF* 168, regarding the typing of *Fungi from Yuggoth.*

Table 2

The notes below are found on the TMS of *Fungi from Yuggoth*. The note "Unpublished poetry" appears in the upper left margin of page 1. (But most poems had been published.) On the upper right is the note "only copy / Please return." Lovecraft's "X" seems to indicate publication, but it is not used consistently. Bracketed items were added to the typescript at dates later than those noted first. "Not available" indicates that the poems had already appeared in copyrighted periodicals. Angle brackets indicate erasures.

I.	TFF / X <Recluse>	XIX.	Weird Tales [not available]
II.	TFF / X <Recluse>	XX.	Prov. Journal [Phantagraph]
III.	TFF / X <Recluse>	XXI.	Weird Tales [not available]
IV.	Driftwind [not available]	XXII.	Weird Tales [not available]
V.	Conover [a] <TFF>	XXIII.	Weird Tales / X [not available]
VI.	Driftwind / X [not available]	XXIV.	Driftwind / X [not available]
VII.	Driftwind / X [not available]	XXV.	
VIII.	Driftwind / X [not available]	XXVI.	Driftwind [not available]
IX.	Weird Tales / X [not available]	XXVII.	Weird Tales [not available]
X.	Ripples / TFF [b]	XXVIII.	X [d]
XI.	Prov. Journal / <TFF> [Phantagraph]	XXIX.	Prov. Journal [e] / X
XII.	Driftwind [not available]	XXX.	Prov. Journal / X [Galleon] [f]
XIII.	Weird Tales / X / F[ine?] [not available]	XXXI.	Prov. Journal [Phantagraph]
XIV.	Weird Tales [not available]	XXXII.	Weird Tales [not available]
XV.	Weird Tales / X [not available]	XXXIII.	Silver Fern / X [Phantagraph] [g]
XVI.	Driftwind [not available]	XXXIV.	[h]
XVII.	Ripples [TFF / X] [c]	XXXV.	Pioneer [i]
XVIII.	Driftwind / X [not available]	XXXVI.	Causerie

a. Lovecraft failed to note that he had submitted "Homecoming" to *Fantasy Fan* and thus inadvertently sent it to Willis Conover for *Science-Fantasy Correspondent* (*LaL* 127).

b. "The Pigeon-Flyers" was published only in *Ripples from Lake Champlain*.

c. "A Memory" did not appear in *Fantasy Fan*.

d. Although marked by an X, "Expectancy" never appeared in a periodical.

e. Lovecraft failed to note that "Nostalgia" was also accepted by *Phantagraph*.

f. *Galleon* had taken two sonnets (22 April 1935, *ET* 307), but the magazine suspended publication before the second, "Harbour Whistles," could appear.

g. Lovecraft does not note that *Galleon* also had accepted the poem, even though it was not published—much as "A Memory" was accepted for but not published by *Ripples from Lake Champlain*.

h. Lovecraft neglected to indicate that "Recapture," which had been published in *WT*, was "not available." Of course when it was published in *WT*, it was not yet a part of *Fungi from Yuggoth*.

i. *Pioneer* also accepted and published "Continuity."

mid-1932, "Evening Star" and "Continuity," the two poems that were not part of Lovecraft's circulating typescript, appeared in Walter M. Stevenson's *Pioneer*.[66]

In 1932, Harold S. Farnese of the Institute of Musical Education, Ltd. in Los Angeles asked Lovecraft if he might set two sonnets of *Fungi from Yuggoth* to music.[67] Lovecraft granted his permission and by September Farnese had written music for "Mirage" and "The Elder Pharos," the poems that had appeared in *Weird Tales* for February–March 1931. He composed the music swiftly upon receiving Lovecraft's permission, for the music bears a copyright date of 1932 (see Appendix E). Lovecraft never saw the sheet music nor heard the pieces played. Farnese later sought to collaborate with Lovecraft on a proposed musical drama in one act set on Yuggoth to have been called *Fen River,* but Lovecraft demurred.

Publication of *Fungi from Yuggoth* abated somewhat until 1934, when Lovecraft began to receive requests from young fans for material for their amateur publications. He complied by submitting short stories and poems unreprinted since their initial appearances in amateur journals, or items that had been rejected or never published. The *Fantasy Fan,* edited by Charles D. Hornig, was the first of the fan publications to print selections from *Fungi from Yuggoth,* and the only one to acknowledge that they were part of a longer piece. "The Book" and "Pursuit" appeared in the October 1934 issue, which was dedicated to Lovecraft. It also accepted "The Key," "Homecoming," and "A Memory" but folded before it could publish "A Memory." In other words, *Fantasy Fan* published the opening three poems of *Fungi from Yuggoth* in sequence, as Lovecraft intended, albeit in two consecutive issues of the magazine. Oddly enough, Duane W. Rimel's long poem *Dreams from Yith* appeared in *Fantasy Fan* before the very poem that inspired it.

In November 1934, Maurice W. Moe had requested "literary contributions to the various magazines of [his] infant charges," and Lovecraft responded that "any of the Fungi from Yuggoth could go to the two who desire respectively 'any poem suitable for a magazine of literary & general

66. There are two typed leaves at JHL that contains both poems, but these were prepared in 1934 by RHB; see Appendix D, items 3c and 4. How HPL transmitted the two poems to *Pioneer* is not clear; he must have typed the two poems without keeping a copy for himself.

67. HPL to ET, [30 July 1932], *ET* 215.

interest' & 'poem on any suitable topick for poetry'."[68] Whether anything came of this is unknown.

Donald A. Wollheim and Wilson Shepherd took five poems—those originally published in the *Providence Journal*—for the *Phantagraph*, though not all at the same time. Lloyd Arthur Eshbach took "Background" and "Harbour Whistles" for the *Galleon* (though only "Background" was published), and Ernest A. Edkins, no youthful fan publisher but an old-time amateur journalist, took "Continuity" for *Causerie*. Wollheim and Shepherd prepared a special publication that consisted of a single poem from *Fungi from Yuggoth*, using one of the five poems Lovecraft had provided. "Background" was published as "A Sonnet" in what was called the "Fourty-Sixth [*sic*] Anniversary Issue" of the *Lovecrafter*.[69] Duane W. Rimel was another fan who requested from Lovecraft material for a prospective publication. By way of reply, Lovecraft wrote: "About the Yuggothian Fungi—would you want to use anything that had been used before? After giving two to Barlow last month for his future paper, I find that the range of *absolutely unpublished* sonnets is wholly exhausted."[70] In September 1935, Lovecraft again told Duane W. Rimel that he could have several of the poems for a magazine he intended to publish with Emil Petaja to be called the *Fantaisiste's Mirror*, but the project never materialized.

Lovecraft forgot that "Homecoming" had been published in the *Fantasy Fan* and inadvertently submitted the poem to Willis Conover, Jr., on 9 July

68. HPL to Maurice W. Moe, Thanksgiving Day [22 November 1934], (*MWM* 365).

69. The *Lovecrafter* was "printed with the deep gratitude and best wishes of Wilson Shepherd and Donald A. Wollheim" as the 20 August 1936 issue (Vol. 47, No. 1). The date is, of course, that of HPL's forty-sixth birthday; the volume number equivalent to the start of HPL's forty-seventh year. Despite the numbering, it was actually the only issue (although Dirk W. Mosig published an "Eighty-Fifth Anniversary Issue" of the *Lovecrafter* in 1975).

70. HPL to Duane W. Rimel, 4 August 1935, *FLB* 280. What these may be is uncertain, because at the time in question HPL was visiting RHB in Florida and so there is no written record of what he may have promised to RHB. Perhaps HPL refers to "Evening Star" and "Continuity," copies of which RHB had typed for HPL not long before. However, RHB never published any poems in a "future paper" (probably intended for his *Dragon-Fly*); neither did Rimel. HPL's statement that there were no "absolutely unpublished" sonnets is an error, unless unknown appearances of "A Memory," "St. Toad's," and "Expectancy" remain to be found. They are not indicated as used on HPL's publication log. Curiously, Barlow published a poem titled "Expectancy" by ET in the first issue of his *Dragon-Fly* (1935).

1936 for the *Science-Fantasy Correspondent*.[71] Lovecraft also submitted "The Pigeon-Flyers," "A Memory," and "Night-Gaunts" and various other poems to Conrad Ruppert and Julius Schwartz for their *Fantasy Magazine*. The poems were not published and were turned over to Willis Conover in January 1937 for use in *Science-Fantasy Correspondent,* but it too expired before the poems could appear. However, Conover published "Homecoming" and the three sonnets originally submitted to *Fantasy Magazine* shortly after Lovecraft's death within an article he wrote for the *Democrat & News,* the newspaper in his hometown of Cambridge, Maryland.[72] This constituted the first appearance of "The Pigeon-Flyers" and "A Memory."

Thirty-three sonnets of *Fungi from Yuggoth* (including "Recapture") made forty-four appearances in print before Lovecraft's death in March 1937, but not the entire sequence. Following his death, a great demand arose for his writings, and *Weird Tales* happily bought stories and poems that it had previously rejected. August Derleth sold nineteen sonnets to *Weird Tales*—eight to editor Farnsworth Wright and eleven to Dorothy McIlwraith—which published them between 1938 and 1947 (see Appendix C).

V.

This is the hour when moonstruck poets know
What fungi sprout in Yuggoth . . .[73]

The biographical description of H. P. Lovecraft that appeared in the anthology *Harvest* in 1933 stated that "His sequence of sonnets, *Fungi from Yuggoth,* have [*sic*] not yet seen book publication."[74] Walter J. Coates, publisher of *Harvest* and the little magazine *Driftwind,* would have been the ideal publisher for the poem, although the focus of his imprint was primarily on the work of Vermonters. The Recluse Press of Lovecraft's associate W. Paul Cook might have been another good possibility. Cook had published

---

71. HPL to Willis Conover, Jr., [postmarked] 18 November 1936, *RB* 402. HPL's typescript had noted that "Homecoming" had gone to the *Fantasy Fan,* but that note was expunged and Conover's name is indicated on the typescript, meaning the note was made at a very late time.

72. "Observations and Otherwise" appeared in the paper for Thursday, 8 July 1937.

73. "XIV. Star-Winds," ll. 9–10.

74. *Harvest: A Sheaf of Poems from* Driftwind 55.

Frank Belknap Long's *A Man From Genoa* (1926), Samuel Loveman's *The Hermaphrodite: A Poem* (1926), John Ravenor Bullen's *White Fire* (1928, edited by Lovecraft), Donald Wandrei's *Ecstasy and Other Poems* (1928), Coates's *Land of Allen and Other Verse* (1928), various little magazines, including the *Recluse,* and even Lovecraft's *The Shunned House* (1928). The books were published at the authors' expense, except for *The Shunned House,* for which Cook was willing to undertake the inherent risk. (In the end, Cook was unable to bind the printed sheets and the book was not officially published.) Lovecraft would not be one to subsidize the publication of a book, especially during the Depression.

It was Lovecraft's young correspondents who first attempted to remedy that, although such projects would have consisted of mimeographed sheets or small booklets, rather than professionally printed and bound books such as Coates or Cook would have made. Earl Kelley may have been the first to contemplate publishing the whole of *Fungi from Yuggoth,* but the book did not progress beyond his simple suggestion.[75] Likewise, an edition planned as early as May 1935 by Louis C. Smith and William F. Anger never materialized.[76] Lovecraft had sent his typescript to Anger, cautioning him to take care to typeset the poem accurately, and offered to read proofs. Smith acknowledged receipt of the poem from Anger in his letter to Lovecraft of 12 June 1935 (ms., JHL) and said that he intended to use a friend's printing apparatus to print the book. By late July, no progress had been made on the book, so Lovecraft urged Smith and Anger to send his typescript to R. H. Barlow if the book could not be done.[77] In mid-August 1935 Lovecraft was certain that the typescript was en route from Smith to Barlow.

R. H. Barlow (1918–1951), who became Lovecraft's literary executor, expressed a desire as early as May 1935 to attempt to publish *Fungi from Yuggoth.*[78] Barlow was an impetuous amateur publisher who brimmed with ideas for projects. Among his proposed publications (aside from *Dragon-Fly* and the more ambitious *Leaves*) was a collection of letters by the late Henry S.

75. Earl C. Kelley to HPL, 29 February 1932 (ms., JHL).
76. HPL to William F. Anger, 1 June 1935, *RB* 238.
77. HPL to William F. Anger, 22 July 1935, *RB* 241.
78. HPL to William F. Anger, 1 June 1935, *RB* 238.

Dim Essences

Whitehead. *Caneviniana* was announced in April 1934 and Barlow set up and printed a few pages, but by August he abandoned the project. Barlow also sought to finish the binding of Lovecraft's *The Shunned House,* which W. Paul Cook had printed in 1928 but was then unable to bind. Barlow bound fewer than a dozen copies be-

The N.E. (left) and S.W. (right) images on the "Carter" stationary.

fore that project, too, was abandoned. When Lovecraft spent his second summer in Florida with the Barlows, he wrote letters to correspondents on stationery designed by Barlow. The art on the stationery (said to be that of "Randolph W. Carter"—Lovecraft's first indication that Carter had a middle name) consisted of four images: "I am especially proud of the Coffin of Lissa motif in the N.W. & S.E. corners. Other parts typify the Fungi from Yuggoth, permeated by subtle colours out of space."[79]

Barlow soon began to make plans for a publishing operation that he called the Dragon-Fly Press. One early project that actually saw completion was a collection of poems by Frank Belknap Long titled *The Goblin Tower,* published as a surprise to the poet. Lovecraft set most of the type for the book himself.[80] Before Barlow completed the book in December, he issued the first number of the *Dragon-Fly* for the National Amateur Press Association on 15 October 1935. The Dragon-Fly Press also hoped to publish a collection of poetry by Elizabeth Toldridge and Clark Ashton Smith's long-planned collection (since 1925), *Incantations.* Smith had provided the poems for his book and even instructed Barlow as to where to insert a few late additions to it. But in the end, both projects came to naught.

Barlow envisioned *Fungi from Yuggoth* as a 48-page booklet bound in heavy green paper and sewn with cord in an edition of 100 copies. Lovecraft

79. HPL to August Derleth, 16 June 1935, *ES* 2.698. "The Coffin of Lissa" was a story by Derleth. The coffin image is not shown here.

80. HPL to Duane W. Rimel, 15 December 1935, *FLB* 307.

told Toldridge in December 1935 that Barlow was just beginning to print *Fungi from Yuggoth*,[81] unaware that Barlow was also preparing a booklet of Lovecraft's "The Cats of Ulthar" as his Christmas card for 1935. Lovecraft surely proofread "The Book," for Barlow had written "2nd proof Dec/35" on a page proof. When Lovecraft returned the proof to Barlow he wrote: "Well, bless my soul! What kind of an enterprise is this which I see under way? Yes—the Fungus is correct, even unto the fi & fl, so far as I can see. Won't have to return the proof. But don't waste too much time on junk like this!"[82] Barlow tinkered with additional design changes to the page and on 28 January 1936 produced another proof.

Barlow put aside *Fungi from Yuggoth* at about that time to work on the second number of the *Dragon-Fly* and to commence work on *Incantations*. On 29 January 1936, Lovecraft wrote to Barlow:

> Best wishes for "Incantations"—and don't fail to let me read the proofs. [. . .] Don't bother with the "Fungi" until the CAS venture is complete. By the way—did Louis Smith send you the MS. he had? I have no Fungi MS. whatever on hand at present—one having been sent to him, and the other lent to somebody or other, damned if I know who. Don't put too much energy into de luxe copies that can't be disposed of—for I doubt whether the demand for this classic will be very wide or vociferous.[83]

It does not appear that Barlow set any type for *Incantations*, which appeared in a somewhat different arrangement in Smith's *Selected Poems*, compiled in the late 1940s but not published until 1971. As of February, Smith had still not returned or passed on Lovecraft's typescript: "Damn Louis Smith for not returning my Fungi! And I wish I knew where the *old* MS. is. I patched it up & lent it to somebody—but I can't remember whom. That is the only one with annotations as to where the various items have appeared."[84]

It is unclear why Barlow even needed Lovecraft's typescript. We know of Lovecraft's own (presumably the one lent), his draft, two carbons that

---

81. HPL to ET, 20 December 1935, *ET* 319.

82. HPL to RHB, 13 December [1935], *OFF* 304. HPL refers to the type used to set the fi ligature in "find" (I.14) and the fl in "floor" (I.7).

83. HPL to RHB, 29 January [1936], *OFF* 315.

84. HPL to RHB, [9 February 1936], *OFF* 319.

survive (without "Recapture"), and the typed copy that Barlow had made in 1934. Per Lovecraft's comment, Barlow now had somewhat more grandiose plans for the book—at least some "de luxe copies," though what that may have constituted is unknown. But if neither Barlow nor Lovecraft no longer had the text, then Barlow must have typeset "The Book" from its appearance in the *Fantasy Fan*. It might be that Barlow got an early start on the book using the text from the *Fantasy Fan* but then put *Fungi from Yuggoth* aside until a complete typescript of the poem could be located.

The project lay dormant until Barlow resumed work on it following the publication of the second number of the *Dragon-Fly* on 15 May 1936. The typescript finally must have been received, and so *Incantations* now was put aside.[85] Barlow, unknown to Lovecraft, set up "To a Dreamer," which was not part of the poem but which Barlow may have seen as a kind of preface to it, presumably because of its thematic content and also because of the mention of "the peaks of Thok" in line 13 (cf. XX.9). The page proof for "To a Dreamer" is dated "10 A.M. Sunday, May 31st." When Lovecraft proofread "To a Dreamer" he emphatically noted that the poem was not to be indicated as part of the sonnet sequence, which had been implied by the running head "Fungi from Yuggoth" Barlow had set at the top of the page. Barlow later produced another proof from which the running head was removed, but one imagines that Lovecraft would have preferred that the poem not be included at all.

The work on *Fungi from Yuggoth* progressed fairly smoothly at first, as indicated by Barlow's notes on some of the page proofs:

Pursuit	Proof June 1, 1936
Recognition	First Proof June 19, 1936
The Lamp	Tuesday [probably June 23]
The Port	June 26, 1936
The Pigeon-Flyers	June 29, 1936
The Howler	July 1
Star-Winds	Printed July 6, 1936

85. See *Phantagraph* 4, No. 3 (June 1936) 9: "R. H. Barlow is the owner of the Dragon Fly Press . . . now in process of publication is H. P. Lovecraft's 'Fungi from Yuggoth', and coming is Clark Ashton Smith's 'Incantations'."

The notes "July 20, 1936 / completed" on leaf 8 and "July 21, 1936" on leaf 7 of Barlow's own transcript of the poem coincide with the printing of "The Gardens of Yin" and "Azathoth," respectively. In discussing the book at a later time, Barlow remarked: "I was printing every other one, & intended to go back & fill in—this seemed the best plan when I did it—though now I admit its logic is obscure."[86] In the end, he printed only I, II, IV, VI, VIII, X, XII, XIV, XVI, XVIII, and XXII.

But then Barlow changed his mind—again—about the contents of the volume. Lovecraft responded with impatience and exasperation:

> Now about this matter of The Collected Poetical Works of H. P. Lovecraft—I'll consider it when I have a finished copy of Klarkash-Ton's "Incantations" in my hands. One thing at a time! But even then there won't be much to add. Most of my verse was utter tripe, as you'll see when I shew you some of the old-time specimens for fun. I wouldn't have it printed again for the world! "Nemesis", "Recapture", "The Ancient Track", & "The Outpost" are all right for inclusion—& I'll give a verdict on "The Nightmare Lake" when I have time to burrow for it in my files. [. . .] I have a lot of other old weird verse—some of which I shall let Wollheim & other kid editors reprint in their magazines—but I don't think I'd want it in a collection. However, I'll see when I exhume it. Of non-weird verse perhaps 3 or 4 items are worth preserving—but they ought not to go in a collection predominantly weird.[87]

"Recapture" became integrated into *Fungi from Yuggoth* during June, as the book was being typeset. The reason for its inclusion is unknown. Perhaps Barlow merely thought it preferable not to have a blank page at the end of the poem. His inclination was merely to place "Recapture" at the end, but Lovecraft suggested a more suitable location, as evidenced by various erasures and changes to the surviving typescripts, and also provided further guidance regarding his collected poetical works:

> Bless my soul—*more* work for an old man! Well—here's the correct text of the material you sent—plus some more junk on which I'll comment presently. Looking over the Fungi—I think "Recapture" had better be

---

86. RHB to Groo and Claire Beck, 2 July 1938; in Faig, "The Book That Nearly Was" 121.
87. HPL to RHB, 4 June 1936, *OFF* 338–39.

#34—with "Evening Star" as *35* and "Continuity" as *36*. "Recapture" seems somehow more *specific & localised* in spirit than either of the others named, hence would go better before them—allowing the Fungi to come to a close with more diffusive ideas. As for other stuff—it will have to be confined to the weird. [. . .] I am sending everything that I can think of [. . .] which I wouldn't violently object to seeing in print. [. . .] If, however, any of these poor items (indicated as such on the enclosed "table of contents") may chance to appeal to you, I wouldn't *object* to their inclusion. [. . .] I think the volume better dispense with the elided e's (*doom'd* &c.) & other textual archaisms of which I am so personally fond. [. . .] If you do by chance use the long "Aletheia Phrikodes", *don't use the comic framework*. [. . .] As for *arrangement*—here is a sample table of contents [see Table 3] shewing not only how the half-decent verses ought to go, but where each of the bum ones ought to be inserted if used. Vague relationships & subtle emotional modulations guided my choice of order. I think "Nemesis" ought to come last—as a sort of climax.[88]

By July, Barlow had changed his mind yet again about the contents of the poetry volume, as evidenced by Lovecraft's letter to him of 23 July 1936:

About my verses—yes, I presume it would be most practical to segregate the Fungi and the other junk in separate volumes. I'd want to go over the text of the miscellany before letting it see the light of print. [89]

In the end, and not unexpectedly, the Dragon-Fly Press edition of *Fungi from Yuggoth* was never completed. In mid-1936, the illness of Barlow's father caused the breakup of the family. Barlow's father remained in Florida and his mother moved to Kansas City. Barlow joined his mother after his visit to Lovecraft in Providence from 28 July to 1 September. He enrolled in art school and had to abandon his various printing projects. In all, Barlow had typeset and printed "To a Dreamer," eleven poems of *Fungi from Yuggoth*, and a mockup of the title page with an illustration by Clark Ashton Smith.[90] On

---

88. HPL to RHB, 13 June 1936, *OFF* 341–42. HPL's comments in this letter corroborate the notes written on the TMS. (See Appendix D, item 3c.)

89. HPL to RHB, 23 July 1936, *OFF* 353.

90. CAS to RHB, June 1936 (ms., JHL): "By all means use that little sketch of mine for Fungi from Yuggoth." This was probably an item purchased by or given to RHB, and not something done specifically for the book.

Table 3
Fungi from Yuggoth and other Verses
H. P. Lovecraft
Fungi From Yuggoth, I–XXXVI
Aletheia Phrikodes ?
The Ancient Track
Oceanus ?
Clouds ?
Mother Earth ?
The Eidolon ?
The Nightmare Lake ?
The Outpost
The Rutted Road ?
The Wood
Hallowe'en in a Suburb ?
The City
The House
Primavera
October
To a Dreamer
Despair ?
Nemesis

Note: This table is from a handwritten list prepared by Lovecraft (see *OFF* 348). His question marks indicate doubt as to whether the items indicated should be included.

1 September 1936, Lovecraft informed a correspondent that "No volume of my verse will appear for a long while, since Barlow is moving to Kansas—doesn't know when he can get at his printing & binding apparatus again."[91]

In January 1937, Lovecraft wrote to Barlow, "Glad your present environment shews some indications of stability, & trust you can in course of time transport & reëstablish the Dragon Fly Press & Bindery & other typically Cassian institutions on wild western soil,"[92] but that was not to be. Lovecraft died in March and Barlow's ocular problems prevented him from finishing the project he conceived nearly two years earlier. In the meantime, five sonnets from *Fungi from Yuggoth* that had appeared in the *Phantagraph* were swiftly published in a memorial booklet issued by Corwin F. Stickney of Belleville, New Jersey. *HPL* was issued in an edition of merely twenty-five

91. HPL to William F. Anger, [postmarked 2 September 1936], *RB* 246.
92. HPL to RHB, 3 January 193[7], *OFF* 392.

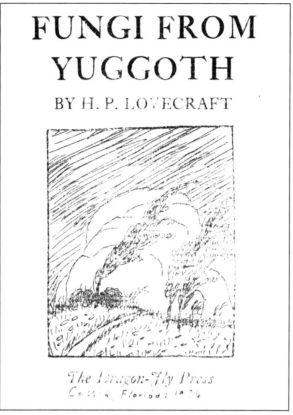

FUNGI FROM YUGGOTH

BY H. P. LOVECRAFT

The Dragon-Fly Press
Cassia, Florida : 1936

Mockup of itle page (detail) for Dragon-Fly Press edition of *Fungi from Yuggoth*.

copies and distributed free to subscribers to Stickney's *Amateur Correspondent*.

In July, Barlow began to correspond with Claire and Groo Beck of Lakeport, California. The Beck brothers presided over the Futile Press, which in May had published Clark Ashton Smith's *Nero and Other Poems*. Barlow and the Becks discussed plans to publish an edition of Smith's *The Hashish-Eater* and several other projects, including Lovecraft's commonplace book. Unfortunately, all Barlow's printing projects came to a standstill in January 1938 when his doctor advised him to cease his literary projects lest he ruin his eyesight. At that time, Barlow offered to turn over *Fungi from Yuggoth* to the Futile Press for completion. Barlow mailed the Becks the paper stock for the book along with the pages he himself had completed.

Lovecraft's death in 1937 took the wind out of Barlow's sails, and his

Printed page (detail) from the Dragon-Fly Press edition of *Fungi from Yuggoth*.

interest in weird literature waned, but not entirely. He published two issues of *Leaves*, an edition of Lovecraft's commonplace book (1938) through
the Futile Press, edited *After Sunset* (1939), a collection of fugitive poems
by George Sterling, and even wrote a few short essays for Arkham House
books. When August Derleth expressed displeasure at Barlow publishing
the *Notes and Commonplace Book*, Barlow asked Derleth repeatedly if Derleth would object to the Futile Press finishing *Fungi from Yuggoth*. Barlow
comments in a letter to Derleth how Derleth objected to its publication
before Farnsworth Wright had exhausted all possibilities for publication
of the sonnets first in *Weird Tales*,[93] but Derleth also wrote "I do suggest
that for the present you let no material be printed by Futile or anyone
else."[94] Individual sonnets continued to appear in 1939 and 1940, and, sadly,
the Dragon-Fly/Futile Press edition of *Fungi from Yuggoth* was never completed. The dummy of the book that Barlow had sent to Derleth was never
returned to him, although Derleth eventually deposited it at the John Hay
Library where it can be seen today.

93. RHB to August Derleth, [late June 1938] (ms., Wisconsin Historical Society).
94. August Derleth to RHB, 2 July [1938] (ms., Wisconsin Historical Society).

No attempt was made to publish the complete poem until around June 1943, when William H. Evans circulated the poem (probably no more than sixty-five copies) through the Fantasy Amateur Press Association. Only thirty-three of the thirty-six sonnets were printed. As noted, for years Lovecraft had circulated a typescript of the poem that did not include the two poems he had always intended to be the closing items. Apparently Evans's source for the poem was itself lacking the final poems, and Evans was unaware that there were additional poems. But the source of his text muſt have been a copy of Lovecraft's typescript, made some time before Lovecraft and Barlow eſtablished the final text of thirty-six sonnets.

The following adds further confusion to the matter of early publication of *Fungi from Yuggoth* without the concluding sonnets:

FUNGI FROM YUGGOTH. 1943, F. T. Lanley [*sic*]. In a letter to Harold Wakefield dated February 12th., 1943 Lanley mentions that he has a copy of "Fungi From Yuggoth" that had been typed and sent to him by HPL. Unfortunately Lanley neglects to mention if this copy is in any way distinguishable, however a similar copy has been seen inscribed by HPL to C. A. Smith, and since HPL often personalized correspondence, hoepfully [*sic*] this and other such copies, when found, can be authenticated. In April 1943 Lanley sends Wakefield a copy of "Fungi from Yuggoth" typed directly from the copy he had received from HPL. It consists of eleven 8½ by 11 sheets typed rectos only, side stapled, signed by Lanley and dated March 43. Lanley also mentions photocopying HPL's original and sending copies out to friends. In all cases the laſt three sonnets are omitted. . . .[95]

It is difficult to know what to make of this statement. There is no evidence that Lovecraft ever corresponded with Francis T. Laney (1914–1958).[96] Laney was the editor of the *Acolyte*, the first issue of which appeared in 1942. Harold Wakefield, a Canadian fan, was a contributing editor, along with F. Lee Baldwin and Duane W. Rimel (these latter two had corresponded with Lovecraft). Lovecraft had lent *Fungi from Yuggoth* to Rimel on 22 January 1934. Rimel's *Dreams from Yith* clearly was inspired by Lovecraft's poem. The

95. Bell 5.
96. Although certainly old enough to have corresponded with HPL, Laney's name and address are not among those of other correspondents in the liſt RHB compiled for Auguſt Derleth in March 1937. HPL's letters do not mention Laney.

statement that Laney both had a copy of *Fungi from Yuggoth* "sent to him by HPL" and had photocopied "HPL's original" is highly doubtful, but he certainly had obtained the text somehow. At this writing, L. W. Currey offers for sale "FUNGI FROM YUGGOTH" [poems]. TYPED MANU-SCRIPT (TMS). 11 pages typed on rectos of eleven sheets of 8½ × 11-inch plain paper, side stapled. Fair copy, carbon, made by Francis T. Laney, circa 1941. A presentation copy with signed inscription by Laney on verso of last sheet: "To / Harold Wakefield / from / Francis T. Laney / March 1943."[97] It is not known how Currey dates the carbon to 1941, but that date is surely possible. Since the carbon was "made by Laney," he presumably had a top copy, and since he typed a copy of the poem, he must have obtained a copy from someone else. As Currey suggests, it was probably from Laney or Wakefield that Bill Evans obtained the text for his FAPA publication.

It may be that someone associated with the *Acolyte* borrowed or obtained a typescript of the poem from Lovecraft, R. H. Barlow, or someone else who may have obtained or made a copy of the poem such as Louis C. Smith or Duane W. Rimel. Another possible source would have been Clark Ashton Smith, who himself had received a carbon from Barlow.[98] Smith was in contact with various of the California fans in the early 1940s.

In any case, at long last, some fourteen years after composition and six years after Lovecraft's death, *Fungi from Yuggoth* was published in its entirety in the second Lovecraft omnibus to emerge from Arkham House, *Beyond the Wall of Sleep* (1943). Arkham House included the poem in the anthology *Dark of the Moon: Poems of Fantasy and the Macabre* (1947) and showcased it in Lovecraft's *Collected Poems* (1963), reprinted in paperback as *Fungi from Yuggoth and Other Poems* (1971). Lovecraft's other poetry saw only sporadic preservation until 2001 with the publication of *The Ancient Track: The Complete Poetical Works of H. P. Lovecraft. Fungi from Yuggoth* has remained the most popular of his verse and has been reprinted in several small press editions in recent years.

97. www.lwcurrey.com/pages/books/108104/lovecraft/fungi-from-yuggoth-poems-typed-manuscript-tms-11-pages-typed-on-rectos-of-eleven-sheets-of-8-1-2-x-11. [October 2015]

98. CAS to RHB, 12 September 1934 (ms., JHL): "thank you for the muchly prized transcript of Fungi From Yuggoth." CAS later incorporated corrections (including two dropped lines), sent to him by HPL or RHB.

VI.

I live in such worlds of endurable memory & dream & cosmic expansion
& escape as my feeble creative powers are able to devise for me—always
staving off the suicide-line by illusions of some future ability to get down
on paper that quintessence of adventurous expectancy which the sight of
a sunset beyond strange towers, or a little farmhouse against a rocky hill,
or a rocky monolith in Leng as drawn by Nicholas Roerich, invariably
excites within me.[99]

It has been stated that *Fungi from Yuggoth* is like a story that must be read in
order from beginning to end to grasp fully the narrative thread.[100] However, that dictum contradicts Lovecraft's statement that "aside from the
introductory three they are meant for independent publication,"[101] and
thus independent comprehension. Lovecraft's use of the plural to describe
the poem (i.e., as "they" rather than "it," and also by referring humorously
to each individual sonnet as a "fungus," but collectively as "fungi") indicates that he thought of the sonnets as individual and distinct items. But
since he gave the series of poems an overarching title and numbered the
poems consecutively, we must recognize the poem as a long, unified work,
but perhaps not "unified" in any conventional sense.

As in the case of much of Lovecraft's fiction, the poem has no strong
plot and its events do not occur linearly. There is no cumulative effect to
be gained by reading all the component sonnets in their numbered order.
The reason for this is simple. Since Lovecraft was working in a relatively
strict poetic form, he did not have space available to develop each vignette
as thoroughly as he might a story. He had to achieve the effect he sought
in the space of fourteen lines, and then within the strictures of a closed
poetic form. He might have written the sonnets as steps that proceeded to
develop a story line, but instead we find poems that are self-contained,
non-linear, occasionally clustered in small groups, but not by any means a

---

99. HPL to Frank Belknap Long, Jr., 27 February 1931, *SL* 3.321.

100. See R. Boerem, "The Continuity of the *Fungi from Yuggoth*"; Ralph E. Vaughan, "The
Story in *Fungi from Yuggoth*"; Robert M. Price, "Second Thoughts on the *Fungi from Yuggoth*";
Phillip A. Ellis, "Unity in Diversity: *Fungi from Yuggoth* as a Unified Setting"; and Robert H.
Waugh, "The Structural and Thematic Unity of *Fungi from Yuggoth*."

101. HPL to ET, [11 February 1930], *ET* 127.

gradually unfolding tale that comes to closure in the final sonnets. Neither end is well suspected at the beginning, and the gradually unfolding story develops as the events occurred to the narrator. However atypical the story line of the poem may be, it nevertheless contains elements he developed in his fiction that will shed light on the way it might be read.

In a letter written to Clark Ashton Smith only days before the poem was begun, Lovecraft described an effect he hoped to achieve in something he hoped soon to write, presumably a story but perhaps not:

> About that "interplanetary" idea of mine—it would begin as a dream-phenomenon creeping on the victim in the form of recurrent nightmares, as a result of his concentration of mind on some dim trans-galactic world. Eventually it would enmesh him totally—leaving his body to vegetate in a coma in some madhouse whilst his mind roamed desolate & unbodied for ever above the half-litten stones of an aeon-dead civilisation of alien Things on a world that was in decay before the solar system evolved from its primal nebula. [. . .] I would try to achieve [. . .] the sense of awesome, utter, & almost mind-unhinging *tremendousness* implicit in the *very notion* of transportation to another world either in body or in mind. [. . .] the whole thing would be more of a psychological study than an adventurous narrative.[102]

This notion coincides with another expressed in a note in Lovecraft's commonplace book, dating approximately to that time: "Adventures of a disembodied spirit—thro' dim, half familiar cities & over strange moors—thro' space & time—other planets & universes in the end" (entry 156).

It is not certain that Lovecraft planned to execute his interplanetary idea as fiction. In their correspondence, Smith assumes that Lovecraft planned a story, and says so several times. But it seems Lovecraft may have attempted to execute his interplanetary idea in verse, for he began *Fungi from Yuggoth* only eight days following his letter to Smith. *Fungi from Yuggoth* clearly embodies that idea, which he explored further in "The Whisperer in Darkness," *At the Mountains of Madness,* and "The Shadow out of Time." Following the acquisition of the mysterious book mentioned in the first three sonnets, "recurrent nightmares" seem to begin with "Recogni-

---

102. HPL to CAS, 19 December 1929, *DS* 194.

tion," where the narrator's mind is concentrated on the gray planet Yuggoth "past the starry voids." The narrator's mind roams freely through both time and space during the course of the poem, most notably in "Alienation." The poem might be said to be, as he described to Smith, "a psychological study [rather] than an adventurous narrative," in that we learn what contributes to the psychological make-up of the narrator (and Lovecraft) as seen from various points of view.

Fungi from Yuggoth is a congeries of dreams, memories, and real events, and it is sometimes difficult to distinguish among them. Lovecraft describes the indistinct difference between various states of consciousness repeatedly in his stories. The following paragraph from "Beyond the Wall of Sleep" is but one examination of the vague boundaries between sanity and madness, between conscious thought and subconscious dreams and memories:

> Whilst the greater number of our nocturnal visions are perhaps no more than faint and fantastic reflections of our waking experiences . . . there are still a certain remainder whose immundane and ethereal character permits of no ordinary interpretation, and whose vaguely exciting and disquieting effect suggests possible minute glimpses into a sphere of mental existence no less important than physical life, yet separated from that life by an all but impassable barrier. From my experience I cannot doubt but that man, when lost to terrestrial consciousness, is indeed sojourning in another and uncorporeal life of far different nature from the life we know; and of which only the slightest and most indistinct memories linger after waking. From those blurred and fragmentary memories we may infer much, yet prove little. We may guess that in dreams life, matter, and vitality, as the earth knows such things, are not necessarily constant; and that time and space do not exist as our waking selves comprehend them. Sometimes I believe that this less material life is our truer life, and that our vain presence on the terraqueous globe is itself the secondary or merely virtual phenomenon. (*CF* 1.71)

Lovecraft's aim in writing never was to concoct compelling plots but rather to create impressions and moods. Indeed, he referred to "The Colour out of Space" as a prose poem. *Fungi from Yuggoth* is a collection of such impressions, just as he described to Smith before undertaking the poem. The reader can savor the atmosphere created in the short space of each individual poem, completely independently of the others. For instance, "St. Toad's" builds a certain eeriness with its thrice-repeated warning, "Beware St. Toad's cracked chimes!", culminating in the narrator's fated discovery of the dreaded church. The episode neither follows from the previous sonnet nor leads into the next one. It is self-contained. *Fungi from Yuggoth* has been called "a description of a dream journey,"[103] as though each sonnet leads the reader down a specific path, but the poem is more nearly a sampling of various dreams and memories that the book mentioned in the opening sonnets arouses in the narrator. The dreams and memories do not necessarily occur in a single event and may represent many different experiences over time, since they are separated by several reflective sonnets (such as "Expectancy," "Background," and "Continuity") placed throughout the poem.

It cannot be denied that there are indeed links between certain successive sonnets. Lovecraft himself said that I, II, and III were linked somehow, and that "aside from the introductory three they are meant for independent publication."[104] IX and X are set in the Hell's Kitchen section of New York City; XVII and XVIII, the imagery of which was lifted nearly verbatim from a paragraph in "Celephaïs," share the same scene; XXI and XXII obviously are related. Even so, there are no direct links between these sonnet pairs and the sonnets that precede and follow them. There are clusters of related events and scenes in the poem, but as far as a continuous story line or a single plot, there is none. In this way, *Fungi from Yuggoth* basically encapsulates Lovecraft's fiction in miniature. Just as many of his stories occur in different periods of time and locales but are loosely interrelated, nearly always against the same cosmic background, the sonnets of *Fungi from Yuggoth* are brief tales that are loosely related parts of a larger pattern that is hinted at but not meticulously outlined.

Lovecraft's own dream experiences may illuminate the form of the poem. He once explained to Willis Conover, Jr.:

> My own dreams usually go back very far in time, & it takes a long while for any new experience or scene or acquaintance to get worked into them.

103. Boerem [222].
104. HPL to ET, [11 February 1930], *ET* 127.

At least ¾ of them are laid at my birthplace, where I haven't lived since 1904, & involve those who were living in those days. But the real scenes frequently merge into unknown & fantastic realms, & include landscapes & architectural vistas which could scarcely be on this planet. [. . .] Many of my "Fungi from Yuggoth" are actual dreams versified.[105]

Similarly, the narrators of *Fungi from Yuggoth* (there seem to be more than one) describe various dreamlike events. Since many of the sonnets of the poem are Lovecraft's "actual dreams versified," they obviously are related only in the sense that he himself dreamt them, and there is no especial significance to the order in which they were dreamt. In addition, *Fungi from Yuggoth*, just as Lovecraft's own dreams, contains scenes both fantastic and real.

Lovecraft's comment to Clark Ashton Smith of 20 November 1931 may also give some insight into the impetus behind the narrative of *Fungi from Yuggoth*:

I am essentially a static, contemplative, & objective person; almost a hermit in daily life, & always preferring to observe rather than to participate. My natural—& only genuine—form of imagination is that of *passive witnessing*—the idea being that of a sort of floating, disembodied eye which sees all manner of marvellous phenomena without being greatly affected by them. I am constitutionally unable to see anything interesting in mere *motions & events*. What absorbs me are *conditions, atmospheres, appearances,* & intangible things of that kind. My perspective is too inherently cosmic & analytical to make me feel the importance of what the tri-dimensional world regards as changes in the relative setting of dust-grains as negligible as terrestrial men. The only things I can conceive as worthy protagonists of cosmic drama are *basic natural forces & laws*, & what spells *interest* for me is simply the convincing illusion of the thwarting, suspension, or disturbance of such forces & laws. To me a climax is simply an effective demonstration of a temporary defeat of the cosmic order. I use human puppets as symbols, but my interest is not with them. It is the situation of defeat itself—& the sensation of liberation therein implicit—which provides me with the thrill & catharsis of aesthetic endeavour. (*DS* 333)

105. HPL to Willis Conover, Jr., 10 January 1937, *RB* 413.

Lovecraft's other writings offer hints to show that *Fungi from Yuggoth* is not a story with a specific plot thread. Experiences described in his stories, particularly dreams, parallel the dream phenomena in his poem. Consider the following example from "Beyond the Wall of Sleep":

> Blending with [the] display of palatial magnificence, or rather, supplanting it at times in kaleidoscopic rotation, were glimpses of wide plains and graceful valleys, high mountains and inviting grottoes; covered with every lovely attribute of scenery which my delighted eye could conceive of, yet formed wholly of some glowing, ethereal, plastic entity, which in consistency partook as much of spirit as of matter. As I gazed, I perceived that my own brain held the key to these enchanting metamorphoses; for each vista which appeared to me, was the one my changing mind most wished to behold. Amidst this elysian realm I dwelt not as a stranger, for each sight and sound was familiar to me; just as it had been for uncounted aeons of eternity before, and would be for like eternities to come. (*CF* 1.81)

Fungi from Yuggoth gives the reader the impression that the sequence of events is not linear. Certainly, Lovecraft wrote many stories in which the events do not occur linearly. In fact, he gave instruction to aspiring writers on how to plan a story's order of occurrence in contrast to the order of narration.[106] He employs flashbacks and other narrative techniques to weave back and forth through the story, to infuse awe and mystery into the events unfolding therein. But those are examples of narrative technique. There are occasions in Lovecraft's works when discontinuity of time is profoundly unsettling. The most obvious example can be found in "The Shadow out of Time":

> My conception of *time*—my ability to distinguish between consecutiveness and simultaneousness—seemed subtly disordered; so that I formed chimerical notions about living in one age and casting one's mind all over eternity for knowledge of past and future ages. (*CF* 3.373)

> Then came that queerness about the element of *time*, and with it desperate efforts to place the fragmentary dream-glimpses in the chronological and spatial pattern. (*CF* 3.377)

---

106. As described in "Suggestions for Writing Story" among his "[Notes on Weird Fiction]" (*CE* 5.169–71).

Fungi from Yuggoth itself is a narrative that consists of "fragmentary dream-glimpses" without "chronological and spatial pattern."

In Lovecraft's stories, the distinctions between waking reality and dreams and memories can be hazy and confused. This is not to say that the events in the stories are essentially identical, but to show the degree to which perception of reality can vary. *Fungi from Yuggoth* characterizes such disorientation as it shifts from present to past to future, and from first- to third-person points of view. How else can we account for the destruction of the world midway through the poem in "Nyarlathotep"; the use of the future subjunctive in "The Gardens of Yin" (as opposed to the present and past tenses that prevail in *Fungi from Yuggoth* overall); and the quiet resolution of everything in "Continuity," the final sonnet?

Just as Lovecraft did not always tell a story in strict chronological order,[107] many of his stories are not told directly by the narrator alone. In "The Call of Cthulhu," various subnarratives that occur in different periods of time are told by various narrators, but all through the voice of Francis Wayland Thurston, the narrator or scribe of the story itself. In "The Colour out of Space," the reader tends to forget that he actually hears Ammi Pierce's tale from the surveyor who relates the story. Likewise, the narrator of the opening sonnets of *Fungi from Yuggoth* is not identical to all the voices of the remaining sonnets, though each poem remains part of his larger story. He is the direct narrator of most sonnets, but it would seem that he is not the narrator of sonnets XI and XXII. The cultivated narrator of "Background" and "Continuity" is surely not the person who elsewhere says "Till funny lines got creased into his face" (XXVI.7).[108]

---

107. See S. T. Joshi's "The Structure of Lovecraft's Longer Narratives" regarding narrative technique in HPL's more ambitious tales. HPL himself advised in "Notes on Writing Weird Fiction": "Prepare a synopsis or scenario of events in the order of their absolute *occurrence*—not the order of their narration. . . . Prepare a second synopsis or scenario of events—this one in order of *narration* (not actual occurrence) . . . Write out the story—rapidly, fluently, and not too critically—following the *second* or narrative-order synopsis" (*CE* 2.176).

108. It is doubtful that HPL consciously employed a technique such as that used by William Faulkner in *As I Lay Dying*, whereby any character speaks aloud in his own speaking voice, but his internal thoughts are uttered in a somewhat loftier and less individualistic language. The deep emotions of the characters are expressed in more universal mental language common to all, but their *speech* as individuals is indicative of upbringing and schooling, or lack thereof.

It must be remembered that *Fungi from Yuggoth* was an experiment. Lovecraft adopted the form of Donald Wandrei's *Sonnets of the Midnight Hours*, which also do not tell a continuous story but are nevertheless related because each individual sonnet describes a nightmare had by only its narrator, who may or may not be the same narrator for each sonnet. In discussing his own poem, Lovecraft noted that "Most of these sonnets represent odd moods & images which have been flitting around in my head for ages—& in several cases I intend to use the themes over again in prose fiction."[109] Thus, Lovecraft clearly considered the episodes of *Fungi from Yuggoth* to be self-contained but not related consecutively, because they constitute notions that occurred to him throughout his life. Rather, they are related much the same way "The Call of Cthulhu," "The Whisperer in Darkness," *At the Mountains of Madness*, and other stories are related. In later years, Lovecraft did indeed write longer stories using ideas from the individual poems in *Fungi from Yuggoth*. "Antarktos" has some bearing on *At the Mountains of Madness*, "St. Toad's" on "The Shadow over Innsmouth," and "The Familiars" on "The Whisperer in Darkness," but those stories should not be considered merely the sonnets writ large.

Fungi from Yuggoth was not outlined ahead of time, as were many of Lovecraft's stories, but was written spontaneously using ideas from his commonplace book and augmented by notes jotted on the manuscript page of "The Bells," about midway through composition of the poem (see Appendix A). Such items as "St. Toad's," "Crawling Chaos," "Nyarlathotep," "Green Meadow," and "night-gaunts" were made merely to prompt additional images, or sonnets. Lovecraft crossed out twelve of the notes—some so thoroughly that they cannot be read, but some can be seen to have been used in the final poems. He meant to employ more of them, for he declared: "I shall probably grind out a dozen or so more before I consider the sequence concluded. I shall re-use a good many of the ideas in later short stories."[110] But no additional sonnets were written.

It must also be remembered that "Recapture" was not part of the original

---

109. HPL to ET, [11 February 1930], *ET* 127.
110. HPL to ET, late January 1930, *ET* 124.

poem. Its place in the poem near the end cannot have contributed specifically to the closing of the poem, as has been suggested. If Lovecraft had carefully worked out a narrative that required *Fungi from Yuggoth* be read in absolute order to achieve the proper effect, he would not have arbitrarily added another poem to the series six years after its independent composition. Nor would he have said he would "grind out" a dozen or so more pieces, only to let the poem stand unchanged with thirty-five (or -six) poems.

Perhaps the best example of how to read *Fungi from Yuggoth* may be gotten from "The Shunned House," for the events described in the poem resemble the description of Elihu Whipple's dream experience in the story:

> my uncle [Whipple] seized my hand and began to relate a dream whose nucleus of significance I could only surmise with a kind of awe.
>
> He had, he said, floated off from a very ordinary series of dream-pictures into a scene whose strangeness was related to nothing he had ever read. It was of this world, and yet not of it—a shadowy geometrical confusion in which could be seen elements of familiar things in most unfamiliar and perturbing combinations. There was a suggestion of queerly disordered pictures superimposed one upon another; an arrangement in which the essentials of time as well as of space seemed dissolved and mixed in the most illogical fashion. In this kaleidoscopic vortex of phantasmal images were occasional snapshots, if one might use the term, of singular clearness but unaccountable heterogeneity. (*CF* 1.472–73)

Nathaniel Peaslee's dreams and experiences of déja vù are described similarly in "The Shadow out of Time":

> Certainly, many persons have dreamed intrinsically stranger things—things compounded of unrelated scraps of daily life, pictures, and reading, and arranged in fantastically novel forms by the unchecked caprices of sleep. (*CF* 3.382)

The sonnets of *Fungi from Yuggoth* can be considered to be more similar to a group of "snapshots" that can be viewed in any sequence (save for the introductory three) than to a cinema reel that must be viewed from beginning to end to comprehend the story it contains. A stack of snapshots can be examined front to back, back to front, or in any number of other ways—just as paintings in a museum or gallery can be viewed in the order chosen by the viewer–but their collective or massed "meaning" will remain essentially the same regardless of the sequence in which they are observed. *Fungi from Yuggoth* could also be seen to be "unrelated scraps . . . arranged in fantastically novel forms" in the narrator's dreams.

Despite the kaleidoscopic nature of the events of *Fungi from Yuggoth*, there is a single principle that unifies the disparity of images: *continuity*. Lovecraft conveys the emotion evoked by the sense of continuity, which he related in compressed fashion in the poem but which he expressed a bit more clearly (and far less compactly) in letters to correspondents. The following passage from a letter to Clark Ashton Smith perhaps expresses the highly personal emotion best:

> I always demand close correlation with the landscape & historic stream to which I belong, & would feel completely lost in infinity without a system of reference-points based on known & accustomed objects. I take complete relativity so much for granted, that I cannot conceive of anything as existing *in itself* in any recognisable form. What gives things an aspect & quasi-significance to us is the fact that we view them consistently from a certain artificial & fortuitous angle. Without the preservation of that angle, coherent consciousness & entity itself become inconceivable. Thus my wish for freedom is not so much a wish to put all terrestrial things behind me & plunge forever into abysses beyond light, matter, & energy. That, indeed, would mean annihilation as a personality rather than liberation. My wish is perhaps best defined as a wish for *infinite visioning & voyaging power*, yet without loss of the familiar background which gives all things significance. I want to know what stretches *Outside*, & to be able to *visit* all the gulfs & dimensions beyond Space & Time. I want, too, to juggle the calendar at will; bringing things from the immemorial past down into the present, & making long journeys into the forgotten years. But I want the familiar Old Providence of my childhood as a perpetual base for these necromancies & excursions—& in a good part of these necromancies & excursions I want certain transmuted features of Old Providence to form parts of the alien voids I visit or conjure up. I am as geographic-minded as a cat—*places* are everything to me. Long observation has shewn me that no other objective experience can give me even a quarter of the kick I can extract from the sight of a fresh landscape or urban vista whose antiquity & historic linkages are such as to correspond

with certain fixed childhood dream-patterns of mine. Of course my twilight cosmos of half-familiar, fleeting remembered marvels is just as unattainable as your Ultimate Abysses—this being the real secret of its fascination. Nothing really known can continue to be acutely fascinating—the charm of many familiar things being mainly resident in their power to symbolise or suggest unknown extensions & overtones. This, then, is our main difference. You want to venture forth into the infinite as a permanent colonist, losing yourself in its exotic marvels as Lafcadio Hearn lost his European entity amidst the exoticism of Japan. I, on the other hand, am like the explorers & adventurers of my ancestral county of Devon—eager to sail the uttermost seas of mystery & avid to behold the nethermost oceans of the void, yet always wishing to keep a calm, familiar, accustomed, old-fashioned English fireside to come back to. My zest for the iridescent gulfs beyond the sunset is reduced by one-half if I cannot glimpse them above an horizon of familiar ancient spires & steep roofs—or more strictly an horizon of *strange* spires & steep roofs, *vaguely suggesting* some lost horizon which was *once* familiar to me. In some, this mixed antiquarianism & exoticism might produce a hopeless emotional conflict; but in me the two elements have so far seemed complementary rather than antagonistic. Anyway, it gives one something to be interested in—& the hope of partly pinning down some of these fleeting dream-glimpses on paper gives one at least a partial reason for remaining alive & conscious.[111]

Fungi from Yuggoth, then, is a collection of pictures whose relationship we cannot know with certainty. Part of it consists of dreams, part of events that occur in the real world, part of memories, and part of visions of the future. Since the events of the poem occur throughout time and space, the scope of the poem is too narrow in which to relate the poem in the same detail found in his fiction. Lovecraft chose instead to produce a group of "photographs" related thematically and emotionally that collectively evoke a certain mood or impression. It is that mood, not a plot, that gives the seemingly disjointed poems of *Fungi from Yuggoth* an overall unity and power.

111. 7 November 1930, *DS* 263–64.

Notes

F*ungi from Yuggoth* is an encapsulization in 504 lines not only of the whole of Lovecraft's life up to the time of its composition, as expressed moSly in his letters and fiction, but also the essence of his later writings. These notes are intended to shed light on the origins of the poem (there are many) and also to show how the images, concepts, and even phrasings of the poem permeate all Lovecraft's writings. Discarded lines (only those few that can be readily deciphered) are provided in the notes merely to illuminate Lovecraft's creative thought.

Fungi from Yuggoth

The title of the poem conStitutes the firSt use of *Yuggoth,* a word of Lovecraft's invention that he said "has a sort of Arabic or Hebraic caSt, to suggeSt certain words passed down from antiquity in the magical formulae contained in Moorish & Jewish manuscripts" (HPL to Duane W. Rimel, 14 February 1934, *FLB* 140–41). In "Some Notes on a Nonentity," Lovecraft wrote how in 1919 he discovered the work of Lord Dunsany, "from whom I got the idea of the artificial pantheon and myth-background represented by 'Cthulhu', 'Yog-Sothoth', 'Yuggoth', etc." (*CE* 5.209–10). Dunsany's *The Gods of Pegāna* contains a tale called "Yug the Prophet." See *OED* s.v. *Yug, yuga:* "In Hindu cosmology, any of the four ages in the duration of the world, the four ages comprising 4,320,000 years and conStituting a great yuga (*Mahāyuga*)." It is not known whether Lovecraft knew anything of Hindu cosmology. The yugas are discussed in the works of the ThesophiSts, but Lovecraft did not read their works, knew of them only in passing, and only got his firSt introduction to their work from E. Hoffmann Price in 1933. Still, see "The Shadow out of Time": "A few of the myths had significant connexions with other cloudy legends of the prehuman world, especially those Hindoo tales involving Stupefying gulfs of time and forming part of the lore of modern theosophiSts" (*CF* 3.385).

Lovecraft conceived of Yuggoth as a planet beyond our own galaxy, since he describes it as being "past the starry voids" (IV.12); however, in "The Whisperer in Darkness" (begun 24 February 1930), he made Yuggoth equivalent to the newly discovered planet Pluto, describing it as "the youngest child, rolling alone in the black aether at the rim" (*CF* 2.487) and as "only the stepping-stone" (*CF* 2.503) to still more distant planets. Unlike the other planets of our solar system, Yuggoth is inhabited. As noted in "The Whisperer in Darkness," "There are mighty cities on Yuggoth—great tiers of terraced towers built of black stone" (*CF* 2.518).

Lovecraft had long been aware of the possibility of a planet beyond Neptune. In youth, he was an avid amateur astronomer and had several telescopes. In a letter to *Scientific American* dated 16 July 1906 he wrote: "In these days of large telescopes and modern astronomical methods, it seems strange that no vigorous efforts are being made to discover planets beyond the orbit of Neptune, which is now considered the outermost limit of the solar system" ("Trans-Neptunian Planets," *CE* 3.16). More than two decades later, his desire to see exploration of the outer reaches of the solar system was realized. Pluto was discovered beyond Neptune on 18 February 1930 by Clyde Tombaugh after ten months of searching. The search for the ninth planet was not publicized, so Yuggoth was not inspired by reporting on Tombaugh's ongoing investigations. His discovery was not announced until 13 March 1930, the one hundred forty-seventh anniversary of the discovery of Uranus and the seventy-fifth anniversary of the birth of Percival Lowell, who had himself searched for a trans-Neptunian planet. Of course, Lovecraft had completed *Fungi from Yuggoth* more than a month before the actual discovery, and two months before the announcement was made. Long before he had written of Lowell's conjecture about such a planet in "Are There Undiscovered Planets?" (*CE* 3.29–30).

During the time Lovecraft was writing "The Whisperer in Darkness," he wrote to Elizabeth Toldridge (1 April 1930):

you have no doubt read reports of the discovery of a new trans-Neptunian planet . . . . a thing which excites me more than any other happening of recent times. Its existence is no surprise, for observers have long known that one or more such worlds probably exist beyond Neptune; yet its actual finding carries hardly less glamour on that account. Keats (thinking no doubt of Herschel's discovery of Uranus in 1781, or perhaps the finding of the earlier asteroids) caught the magic of planetary discovery in two lines of his Chapman's Homer sonnet, & that magic is surely as keen today as then. Asteroidal discovery does not mean much—but a major planet—a vast unknown world—is quite another matter. I have always wished I could live to see such a thing come to light—& here it is! The first real planet to be discovered since 1846, & only the *third* in the history of the human race! One wonders what it is like, & what dim-litten fungi may sprout coldly on its frozen surface! [Cf. XIV.9–10] I think I shall suggest its being named "Yuggoth"! (*ET* 139)

Venetia Burney (1918–2009), an eleven-year-old schoolgirl in Oxford, England, interested in classical mythology and astronomy, suggested to her grandfather Falconer Madan, a former librarian at the Bodleian Library, that the planet be named *Pluto*. Her suggestion was cabled to colleagues in the United States. The object was officially named on 24 March 1930 (in preference to Minerva and Cronus), and the name was announced on 1 May.

The "magic" Lovecraft speaks of is voiced in Keats's "On First Looking into Chapman's Homer" (1816): "Then felt I like some watcher of the skies / When a new planet swims into his ken" (ll. 9–10). In July 2015, the New Horizon space probe, launched in January 2006, passed by Pluto and its moons, sending back astonishing close-up photographs of what Tombaugh saw only as a pinpoint of light on a photographic plate. The fly-by allowed astronomers to see with clarity numerous physical features of the planet's surface. A dark patch near the south pole, initially called "the Whale," ultimately was named the "Cthulhu Regio" in Lovecraft's honor.

What Lovecraft meant by "fungi from Yuggoth" is not clear, but the notion of otherworldly vegetation permeates his writings and may have several sources. *The Hashish-Eater; or, The Apocalypse of Evil* (1920) by Clark Ashton Smith seems to be one. Lovecraft admired the poem and quoted the following passage as a favorite in a letter to Smith of 25 March 1923 following receipt of the poet's *Ebony and Crystal* (1922):

> I delight in your use of the cosmos instead of merely the *world* as a background; you can't imagine—or then again you probably *can*—the pictures that flit through my mind at lines like

> "... I know the blooms
> Of bluish fungus, freak'd with mercury
> That bloat within the craters of the moon,
> And in one still selenic hour have shrunk
> To pools of slime & foetor ..." (*DS* 48)

Other references by Lovecraft to Smith's writings and paintings pertain to otherworldly fungi: "Mr. Smith ... take[s] infinity as his canvas and record[s] in awe ... polychrome fungi more remote than Algol and Achernar" ("[Review of *Ebony and Crystal* by Clark Ashton Smith]," *CE* 2.74); "dank morasses of spotted death-fungi in spectral countries beyond earth's rim" ("Supernatural Horror in Literature," *CE* 2.111); and the "lunar fungi that Clark Ashton Smith uses to freeze the blood" ("Pickman's Model," *CF* 2.63).

In "The Outpost," Lovecraft previewed the turreted domes and cities that later appeared in his sonnet sequence using an image with fungi:

> Strange turrets rose beyond the plain,
>   And walls and bastions spread around
>   The distant domes that fouled the ground
> Like leprous fungi after rain. (*AT* 77–78.13–16)

Aside from the title of the poem, the "fungi from Yuggoth" are mentioned only once (and vaguely at that) in the entire sequence and seem to resemble vegetation, since they "sprout" (XIV.10). But fungi are organisms classified as the kingdom *Fungi*, which is separate from plants, animals, bacteria, and protists. In "The Whisperer in Darkness," Lovecraft made them the winged (and thus quite mobile) crustacean-like creatures observed during the Vermont floods—something of a plant/animal combination, as are the Old Ones in *At the Mountains of Madness*. The footprints seen at the Akeley farm are said to have been made by *"the living fungi from Yuggoth"* (*CF* 2.514). On earth there are fungi that live in anaerobic environments, but these are microscopic. In *At the Mountains of Madness*, Lovecraft writes:

> During the Jurassic age the Old Ones met fresh adversity in the form of a new invasion from outer space—this time by half-fungous, half-crustacean creatures from a planet identifiable as the remote and recently discovered Pluto; creatures undoubtedly the same as those figuring in certain whispered hill legends of the north, and remembered in the Himalayas as the Mi-Go, or Abominable Snow-Men. (*CF* 3.104)

Notes

Note that the creatures are considered to be "half-fungous." In a letter to Clark Ashton Smith (c. 25 December 1930, *DS* 285), he referred to them as "semi-material fungoid Things from Yuggoth."

It is worth mentioning that Lovecraft humorously referred to each sonnet in the sequence as a separate "fungus" and to the entire sequence (or even as few as two) in the plural form, *fungi;* e.g., "my 'Fungi' have just come back, & I am enclosing them herewith" (*ET* 124). Indeed, Lovecraft likened each sonnet to a flower. Cf. Charles Baudelaire's dedication in *Les Fleurs du mal*—"To the impeccable poet / to the perfect magician of French letters / to my beloved and revered master & friend / Théophile Gautier / with a sense of the deepest humility / I dedicate these sickly flowers" (p. [3])—to Lovecraft's comment to Farnsworth Wright, upon his submittal to *WT* of a clean typescript of ten sonnets from the poem that Wright selected for publication: "here are your 10 hand-picked Fungi—and may they adorn with appropriate morbidity the unhallowed gardens which bloom betwixt your covers" ("Letters to Farnsworth Wright" 21).

Entry 156 (c. 1928/1929) of Lovecraft's commonplace book captures the essence of *Fungi from Yuggoth:* "Adventures of a disembodied spirit—thro' dim, half-familiar cities & over strange moors—thro' space & time—other planets & universes in the end."

I. The Book

R. H. Barlow has said that the idea for this sonnet originated in a dream (*OFF* 404). Cf. *CB* 144 (1927 or 1928): "Hideous book glimpsed in ancient shop—never seen again"; and *CB* 171 (1929?): "Hideous old book discovered—directions for shocking evocation." Forbidden or ancient tomes abound in Lovecraft; the *Necronomicon* being the prime example.

Lovecraft stated that some of the themes of the individual poems of *Fungi from Yuggoth* were more suited for use in fiction and that he planned to "make stories of them" when he found the opportunity (2 February 1930, *DS* 204). He did indeed use some of the sonnets as sources for later stories, but he also may have attempted to recast the long poem as a work of fiction. Cf. the prose fragment known as "The Book," which seems to date to October 1933:

These cycles of experience, of course, all stem from that worm-riddled book. I remember when I found it—in a dimly lighted place near the black, oily river [cf. XXIV.3–4] where the mists always swirl. That place was very old, and the ceiling-high shelves full of rotting volumes reached back endlessly through windowless inner rooms and alcoves. There were, besides, great formless heaps of books on the floor and in crude bins; and it was in one of these heaps that I found the thing. I never learned its title, for the early pages were missing; but it fell open toward the end and gave me a glimpse of something which sent my senses reeling. [See Appendix B for complete text.]

But because the sonnet sequence is not an actual narrative, as a story or novel might be, Lovecraft soon abandoned as unworkable his attempt to cast the poem as a work of fiction.

1 half-lost] Cf. *At the Mountains of Madness:* "half-lost in a queer antarctic haze" (*CF* 3.70).

1–2 Thurber's description of the visit to Richard Pickman's secret studio in Boston's North End near the waterfront in "Pickman's Model" is echoed in these lines.

2 tangles] Such scenes are common in Lovecraft's fiction. Cf. *At the Mountains of Madness:* "tangle of dark stone towers" (*CF* 3.79); and "a complex tangle of twisted lanes and alleys" (*CF* 3.80). Lovecraft described Boston, the setting of "Pickman's Model," as a "tangle of alleys" (28 November 1936, *SL* 5.361).

quays] Pronounced *kees.* Wharfs where ships are loaded or unloaded.

3 Lovecraft had a strong aversion to marine odors and seafood.

5 lozenge panes] I.e, diamond-shaped window panes, typical of archaic architecture. Cf. "The Festival": "I saw from the diamond window-panes that it [the house] must have been very close to its antique state" (*CF* 1.408); *The Case of Charles Dexter Ward:* "The house was an old peaked relic of the middle seventeenth century with . . . diamond-paned lattice windows" (*CF* 2.243). Numerous other references to such windows occur in Lovecraft's stories.

6–7 In his *In Memoriam: Howard Phillips Lovecraft*, W. Paul Cook described Arthur Eddy's bookstore in Providence as an "immense store lined from floor to ceiling with shelves packed with books classified by authors or subjects. Tables through the center piled with books. The floor heaped with books over which you had to scramble. Large drawers filled with books. A mezzanine floor choked by books. The stairs to the basement cluttered with books. All these upstairs books had been gone over and priced—very moderately priced. Then the basement, to which few were admitted. A huge room with cords of books—and that is the way to describe them. . . . Heaps, piles, a heterogeneous mixture of everything under the sun" (*Lovecraft Remembered* 125–26). The visit Cook describes occurred in November 1927 (see *SL* 2.185–86). His description echoes Lovecraft's own of the heaps of toppled books in the library of the Great Race in "The Shadow out of Time."

7 congeries] A disorderly collection; a mass or heap. The word requires a singular verb. Cf. "The Whisperer in Darkness": "a congeries of contiguous or arcade-linked barns, sheds, and windmill" (*CF* 2.512); *At the Mountains of Madness*: "a shapeless congeries of protoplasmic bubbles" (*CF* 3.150); "The Dreams in the Witch House": "a rather large congeries of iridescent, prolately spheroidal bubbles" (*CF* 3.245); and "The Horror in the Museum": "a congeries of iridescent globes" (*CF* 4.436). *Fungi from Yuggoth* itself is a kind of a congeries.

8 little cost] Cf. Lovecraft's recollection of his first visit to New York City c. April 1922 (HPL to James F. Morton, 12 March 1930; *JFM* 223): "the mystic bookstalls with their hellish bearded guardians . . . . . monstrous books from nightmare lands for sale at a song if one might chance to pick the right one from mouldering, ceiling-high piles." See also "The Bookstall": "Where crumbling tomes upon the groaning shelves / Cast their lost centuries about ourselves" (*AT* iii.17–18).

11–12] Texts containing various secrets abound in Lovecraft's fiction.

14 Cf. the fragment "The Book": "I remember how the old man leered and tittered" (p. 236); and "The Descendant": "He . . . bore it out of the shop

with such precipitate haſte that the old Jew chuckled diſturbingly behind him" (*CF* 2.402).

Discarded lines:

I found it deep down one of those dim lanes
That twiſt through piled-up filth of centuries,
Where crumbling brick & tottering timber

The town was old & dim & on the sea,
And I was dazed with fever at that time
And

II. Pursuit

Cf. *CB* 55: "Man followed by invisible *thing*." The pursuer in this sonnet is not so much invisible as unseen.

3 "Ancient harbour lanes" are typical settings of many of Lovecraft's ſtories, moſt notably "The Feſtival," "The Call of Cthulhu," "Pickman's Model," *The Case of Charles Dexter Ward*, and "The Shadow over Innsmouth."

5 Cf. "The Shunned House" with an "attic, a vaſt raftered length lighted only by small blinking windows in the gable ends" (*CF* 1.454); and "The Shadow over Innsmouth": "Those windows ſtared so speſtrally that it took courage to turn eaſtward toward the waterfront" (*CF* 3.181).

8 Cf. *At the Mountains of Madness:* "the normal outer realm of sun and sky" (*CF* 3.151).

9 The implication here is that the narrator ſtole the book, but in the fragment "The Book," the bookseller refuses payment from the narrator.

13 madding] Archaic: to be mad or aſt madly; cf. the title of Thomas Hardy's novel *Far from the Madding Crowd*, itself a quotation from Gray's *Elegy* (l. 73). Cf. Shakespeare, Sonnet CXIX: "How have mine eyes out of their spheres been fitted, / In the diſtraſtion of this madding fever!" (ll. 7–8).

14 Cf. "The Book": "As I hurried home through those narrow, winding, miſt-choked waterfront ſtreets I had a frightful impression of being ſtealthily followed by softly padding feet" (p. 236).

Notes

Discarded lines:

Down dizzy lengths of ancient lanes I sped

I held the book beneath my coat at pains
To hide myself from sight in such a place;
Hurrying through ancient harbour lanes
From where I came upon that mouldy trace
Of the old lore, & not for safety caring

III. The Key

Title: The key is the simplest and most important recurrent image, symbol, and metaphor in Lovecraft's writings. In "The Tomb," "He," and "The Silver Key," a key—a device used to open a lock—allows access to be gained to another realm of being; to a place otherwise inaccessible. In "The Tomb" a key is used to unlock the family burial crypt, in "He" to unlock a "small, low-arched gate of nail-studded black oak" (*CF* 1.510), and in "The Silver Key" to gain access to the world of Randolph Carter's dreams. Cf. "The Silver Key": "Then one night his grandfather reminded him of a key. The grey old scholar, as vivid as in life, spoke long and earnestly of their ancient line, and of the strange visions of the delicate and sensitive men who composed it" (*CF* 2.79). In other stories, various kinds of keys (i.e., crucial or significant objects or situations) provide such access. In "Beyond the Wall of Sleep," the narrator says "my own brain held the key to these enchanting metamorphoses" (*CF* 1.81)—that is, to his dreams. A related image is the gate or gateway to another world or dimension that often must be unlocked with some sort of key, as the gate in XVIII. (The word gate/gateway is used seven times in the course of the poem.) In VIII, "the winter sunset . . . opens great gates to some forgotten year." Cf. *CB* 135: "Hideous world superimposed on visible world—gate through—power guides narrator to ancient & forbidden book with directions for access." In "Pickman's Model," Richard Upton Pickman, through his paintings, "found a way to unlock the forbidden gate" (*CF* 2.72). Indeed, the transition from "The Key" to "Recognition" (not only from one sonnet to the other, but also by what is implied in their titles) is a passage through a gateway.

From 1926 onward, Lovecraft's stories abound with ciphers to be interpreted with the aid of a "key" of some sort to crack the code. In *The Case of Charles Dexter Ward*, Ward's "mother saw that he was at work on the photostatic copy of the Hutchinson cipher, which he had frequently shewn her before; but in response to her query he said that the Curwen key could not be applied to it" (*CF* 2.276). In "The Dunwich Horror," Professor Armitage attempts to decipher Wilbur Whateley's diary which is written in an artificial alphabet. Cf. "The Book": "For he who passes the gateways always wins a shadow, and never again can he be alone" (p. 236). In "The Key," the book of the first sonnet seems to be the key to "the hidden way / Across the void." Cf. XXXVI.7–8: "locked dimensions . . . out of reach except for hidden keys." Even in a story with a conventional setting, such as "Cool Air," the simple act of walking through a doorway into a room is the transition from a realm of normalcy into a realm of terror. Perhaps Lovecraft's most poignant use of the key/gate image (and also recognition) may be found in "The Shadow out of Time": "Something was fumbling and rattling at the latch of my recollection, while another unknown force sought to keep the portal barred" (*CF* 3.422).

Remember that *Fungi from Yuggoth* was written following Lovecraft's completion of work on Maurice W. Moe's *Doorways to Poetry*. Lovecraft saw the book as unlocking the door to the appreciation of poetry.

3 Cf. "The Book": "I remember how I read the book at last—white-faced, and locked in the attic room that I had long devoted to strange searchings" (p. 236). Charles Dexter Ward, Crawford Tillinghast, and Dr. Eben Spencer (a figure in a particularly vivid dream) performed strange experiments in their attic laboratories, and "when six years old [Lovecraft himself] used to go up in the attic of the old home and browse among the 18th century books exiled there from the library downstairs" (*MF* 2.580).

4–8 In "The Dunwich Horror" the *Necronomicon* is the key by which to open our dimension to Yog-Sothoth, who exists "not in the spaces we know, but *between* them." Furthermore, "*Yog-Sothoth* knows the gate. *Yog-Sothoth* is the gate. *Yog-Sothoth* is the key and guardian of the gate. . . . *Yog-Sothoth* is the key to the gate, whereby the spheres meet" (*CF* 2.434).

6 across the void] Cf. IV.12.

Notes

6–8 Cf. "The Book": "It was a key—a guide—to certain gateways and transitions of which mystics have dreamed and whispered since the race was young, and which lead to freedoms and discoveries beyond the three dimensions and realms of life and matter that we know. Not for centuries had any man recalled its vital substance or known where to find it" (p. 235). In "The Music of Erich Zann," the viol player's music is the key to "the blackness of space illimitable; unimagined space alive with motion and music, and having no semblance to anything on earth" (*CF* 1.289). In "The Shadow out of Time," the ancient book found in the buried library in the Australian desert, written in Nathaniel Peaslee's own hand, is the key (i.e., the explanation or solution) to his strange dreams and "pseudo-memories."

8 demesnes] Manorial land possessed by the lord and not held by tenants; a domain.

11 earth's precisions] Lovecraft's image emphasizes the regularity of the earth's movement in the heavens, which serves as a counterpoint to the irregularity of the narrator's dream-flights. Cf. XXXIII.7: "Zodiac's course."

12 memories of infinitude] Cf. "Hypnos": "There was a night when winds from unknown spaces whirled us irresistibly into limitless vacua beyond all thought and entity. Perceptions of the most maddeningly untransmissible sort thronged upon us; perceptions of infinity which at the time convulsed us with joy, yet which are now partly lost to my memory and partly incapable of presentation to others" (*CF* 1.328–29).

14 attic window] In "The Unnamable," Randolph Carter is the author of a story titled "The Attic Window" that, when published, caused the magazine to be removed from the newsstands.

fumbling] Cf. "The Book": "Then came the first scratching and fumbling at the dormer window" (p. 236); "The Dreams in the Witch House": "he . . . heard the faint fumbling at the door" (*CF* 3.266); the chapter about the narrator's lodging in "The Shadow over Innsmouth"; among others.

IV. Recognition

Cf. *CB* 97: "Blind fear of a certain woodland hollow where streams writhe among crooked roots, & where on a buried altar terrible sacrifices have occur'd . . ." The narrator's recognition of himself (l. 14) is similar to the scene of recognition in Donald Wandrei's poem "The Head" from *Sonnets of the Midnight Hours*. However, only the version of "The Head" published in *Poems for Midnight* (1964) contains this scene (see *Sanctity and Sin* 96). It is not certain that Lovecraft was familiar with that version, which differs significantly from the one he read in *WT* for December 1928 (rpt. in *Dark of the Moon* [1947]).

2 hollow of old oaks] Cf. "A Confession of Unfaith": "When about seven or eight I . . . thought I beheld some of these sylvan creatures [dryads and satyrs] dancing under autumnal oaks" (*CE* 5.146). Wooded hollows abound in Lovecraft's stories.

5 herbage rank and wild] *Rank* means growing vigorously and coarsely; overluxuriant. Cf. "Memory": "Rank is the herbage on each slope" (*CF* 1.86); and XXXIV.10. By way of contrast, see "A Garden": "In the silent sunken pathways springs an herbage sparse and spare" (*AT* 278.7).

6 carved sign] Cf. "The Rats in the Walls": "We noted the Roman inscriptions and unknown altar designs" (*CF* 1.391).

7 Nameless One] Cf. "The Diary of Alonzo Typer": "the Chant . . . evokes the Nameless One" (*CF* 4.590); and the "Magnum Innominandum," the Great Not-to-be-Named, of Lovecraft's famous Roman dream of November 1927 (*MWM* 457–64) and "The Whisperer in Darkness" (*CF* 2.483).

10 In "The Haunter of the Dark," Robert Blake is the author of a story titled "The Feaster from the Stars" (*CF* 3.454).

12 Yuggoth] This constitutes Lovecraft's first mention of Yuggoth, save for the title of the sequence. Cf. *DS* 147 (15 October 1927): "the black planet, Yadoth," a name suggestive of both Yuggoth and Yaddith (XXXII.5). Yuggoth is also mentioned in XIV, "Medusa's Coil," "The Whisperer in Darkness," "Through the Gates of the Silver Key," "The Horror in the Museum," "Out of the Aeons," and "The Haunter of the Dark." In "The Whisperer in Darkness," Henry Akeley writes of "the object mystically hinted at as 'Yuggoth' in certain ancient and forbidden writings" (*CF* 2.503).

past the starry voids] Cf. XXXIII.7: "beyond the Zodiac's course."

V. Homecoming

Following completion of *Fungi from Yuggoth,* Lovecraft described to Maurice W. Moe a recollection of his recently deceased friend Everett McNeil (1862–1929). McNeil had taken Lovecraft through Hell's Kitchen, which provided a stark and unsettling contrast to the fairy-like scenes Lovecraft had seen from afar when he first encountered Manhattan in 1922.

> It is an infernal shame that he couldn't have had a longer period of emancipation from Hell's-Kitchen squalor at the close of his career. The N. Y. terrain will never seem the same to the gang without him, for his naive, characteristic note was so inextricably woven into our folklore. He forms a vital part of that first, fresh, fantastically marvellous impression of the metropolis which I receiv'd before familiarity bred disgust—that elusive, ecstatically mystical impression of exotick giganticism and Dunsanian strangeness and seethingly monstrous vitality which I picked up in 1922, before I knew it too well . . . . . . Cyclopean phantom-pinnacles flowering in violet mist, surging vortices of alien life coursing from wonder-hidden springs in Samarcand and Carthage and Babylon and Ægyptus, breathless sunset vistas of weird architecture and unknown landscape glimpsed from bizarrely balustraded plazas and tiers of titan terraces, glittering twilights that thickened into cryptic ceilings of darkness pressing low over lanes and vaults of unearthly phosphorescence, and the vast, low-lying flat lands and salt marshes of Southern Brooklyn; where old Dutch cottages reared their curved gables, and old Dutch winds stirred the sedges along sluggish inlets brooding gray and shadowy and out of reach of the long red rays of hazy setting suns. And I remember when good old Mac display'd Hell's Kitchen to Little Belknap and me—a first glimpse for both of us. Morbid nightmare aisles of odorous Abaddon-labyrinths and Phlegethontic shores—accursed hashish-dreams of endless brick walls bulging and bursting with viscous abominations and staring insanely with bleared, geometrical patterns of windows—confused rivers of elemental, simian life with half-Nordic faces twisted and grotesque in the evil flare of bonfires set to signal the nameless gods of dark stars—sinister pigeon-breeders on the flat roofs of unclean teocallis, sending out birds of space with blasphemous messages for the black, elder gods of the cosmic void—death and menace behind furtive doors—frightened policemen in pairs—fumes of hellish brews concocted in obscene crypts—49th St.—11th Ave.—47th St.—10th Ave.—9th Ave. elevated—and through it all the little white-

hair'd guide plodding naively along with his head in a simpler, older, love-
lier, and not very possible world . . . . . a sunny, hazy world of Wisconsin
farm-days and green shores of romantick boy-adventure and Utopian
lands of fixt, uncomplex ſtandards and values . . . . . good old Mac! When
will there ever be another like him? [18 January 1930, *MWM* 255–56]

This long description of New York City contains many elements used elsewhere in *Fungi from Yuggoth*.

1 daemon] See *OED*, s.v. *Demon:* "1[a]. In ancient Greek mythology
(= δαίμων): A supernatural being of a nature intermediate between that
of gods and men; an inferior divinity, spirit, genius. . . . Often written
dæmon for diſtinction from . . . [2.] an evil spirit." [1b]. An attendant, min-
iſtering, or indwelling spirit; a genius." Also s.v. *Genius:* "1: with reference
to classical pagan belief: The tutelary god or attendant spirit allotted to
every person at his birth, to govern his fortunes and determine his character, and finally to conduct him out of the world . . ." The daemon (as Nyarlathotep) is referred to again in XXII. There is a daemon named Memory
in the prose poem of that name, who is "wise in lore of the paſt" (*CF* 1.86).
In "Ex Oblivione" there is a daemon named Life.

1–6 Cf. *The Dream-Queſt of Unknown Kadath:* "as Carter ſtood breathless
and expectant on that baluſtraded parapet there swept up to him the
poignancy and suspense of almoſt-vanished memory, the pain of loſt
things, and the maddening need to place again what once had an awesome
and momentous place" (*CF* 2.98–99); and Walter Gilman's vision from the
dream baluſtrade in "The Dreams in the Witch House."

1–9 These lines are comparable to the description of Satan's temptation of
Chriſt: "Next, taking [Jesus] to a very high mountain, the devil showed
him all the kingdoms of the world and their splendour. 'I will give you all
of these' he said, 'if you fall at my feet and worship me'" (Matt. 4:8).

9 sunset's gate] Cf. "To a Young Poet in Dunedin": "palm-framed sunsets
open gates of flame" (*AT* 191.2).

10 lakes of flame] Cf. *CB* 50: *"Phleg´*-e-thon—a river of liquid fire in Hades."
Also Rev. 19:20, 20:10, 14–15: "the lake of fire." Cf. Lovecraft's reference to
a "flame-lit lakelet" in the quatrain he composed in a letter to James F.

Morton of 8 November 1929 (*JFM* 178; also *AT* 173). This image may be nothing more than a poetic description of the sunset referred to in l. 9.

11 gods without a name] Cf. IV.7: "That Nameless One."

VI. The Lamp

Cf. *CB* 146: "Ancient lamp found in tomb—when filled & used, its light reveals strange world." Lovecraft acknowledged the influence of this entry with the late appended note "Fungi." The entry and this sonnet may both have been suggested by an ancient lamp Lovecraft himself owned: "I also 'fell' for one of the ancient pottery lamps whose cheapness is due to the limitless quantities lately excavated—a Grecian affair of about 500 B.C. It sits before me now, enchanting in its glamour, & has already suggested at least one weird story plot to my inspiration" (HPL to Lillian D. Clark, 8 September 1925 [*LFF* 381).

2 Cf. *CB* 141: "Footnote by Haggard or Lang in 'The World's Desire': 'Probably the mysterious & indecipherable ancient books, which were occasionally excavated in old Egypt, were written in this dead language of a more ancient & now forgotten people. Such was the book discovered at Coptos, in the sanctuary there, by a priest of the Goddess. . . . A scribe of the period of the Ramessids mentions another in indecipherable ancient writing'"; "The Statement of Randolph Carter": "that ancient book in undecipherable characters" (*CF* 1.134); "The Call of Cthulhu," in which the Cthulhu bas-relief is covered with indecipherable hieroglyphics; and "Through the Gates of the Silver Key": "The parchment which no man could read" (*CF* 3.278). Lovecraft uses various sorts of indecipherable writings in many of his stories, such as "Dagon," "The Dunwich Horror," *At the Mountains of Madness,* "The Dreams in the Witch House," "The Shadow out of Time," and others.

2 Thebes] Lovecraft alludes to the ancient city in Egypt rather than the one in Greece; note the "hieroglyphics" in l. 3 and also "Egypt" at XXI.1.

9 forty centuries] Forty centuries ago was 2100 BCE, which fell in the Xth Dynasty.

14 In "He," the narrator sees a horrifying vision in a flash of lightning (cf. note on IX.1–8). Cf. *At the Mountains of Madness:* "to that flash of semi-vision can be traced a full half of the horror which has ever since haunted us" (*CF* 3.147). The ancient city of ſtone in Antarctica, described in the passage from which the quotation above was taken, is somewhat akin to the "hollow cliffs" mentioned in l. 1.

Discarded lines:

They found the lamp in no mere Pharaoh's tomb,
But in those caverns by the upper Nile
Where Theban prieſts had feared to

Deep in the crypts \<which\> that Theban prieſts had \<feared\> shunned,
And warned againſt in frightened hieroglyphs,
We found the temple of a world unsunned,
There was a crypt beneath the other vaults
That

Those fears of forty centuries lay light
On our young souls as science led the way
Deeper & deeper in the endless night
Where primal hands had lit the cryptic ray.

VII. Zaman's Hill

Lovecraft said this sonnet may have been suggeſted by *Elsie Venner* (1861), a weird novel by Oliver Wendell Holmes: "I haven't read [*Elsie Venner*] in years, but can ſtill recall the malign aura that hangs about the great hill againſt which the town is built. Possibly that suggeſted my Yuggothian fungus 'Zaman's Hill'" (HPL to R. H. Barlow, 26 October 1934, *OFF* 187). See also Lovecraft to F. Lee Baldwin (27 March 1934, *FLB* 62): "In Wilbraham, for example (where some amazing cases of crime, inceſt, repulsive domeſtic triangles, &c. crop out amongſt the ignorant farming populace), they whisper oddly about a certain hill-shadowed ſtreet in the neighbouring town of Monson where an abnormal profusion of *suicides* occur from year to year."

Title: Cf. "The Ancient Track," written about one month earlier than "Zaman's Hill," in which Zaman's Hill is mentioned twice (*AT* 79.11, 29).

Lovecraft likely did not know that *Zaman* is an Arabic word for time, era, or life. He mentions, tongue-in-cheek, a "ritual of Zaman-ho" in the closing of his letter to Robert Bloch of 11 August 1934 (*RB* 110).

1–2 These lines may describe an actual place. In July 1928, Lovecraft "was taken to . . . Monson to see a dark, damp street in the shadow of a great hill, the houses on the hillward side of which are whispered about because of the number of their tenants who have gone mad or killed themselves" ("Mrs. Miniter—Estimates and Recollections," *CE* 1.384).

4 Cf. "The Shadow over Innsmouth": "Then we reached the crest and beheld the outspread valley beyond, where the Manuxet joins the sea just north of the long line of cliffs that culminate in Kingsport Head and veer off toward Cape Ann. On the far, misty horizon I could just make out the dizzy profile of the Head . . . but for the moment all my attention was captured by the nearer panorama just below me. I had, I realised, come face to face with rumour-shadowed Innsmouth" (*CF* 3.172).

6 man-shunned slope] See "Department of Public Criticism": "'The Haunted Forest', a poem by J. H. Fowler, is almost Poe-like in its grimly fantastic quality. . . . 'Bird-shunned', as applied to the thickets of the forest, is a particularly graphic epithet. Mr. Fowler is to be congratulated upon his glowing imagination and poetical powers" (*CE* 1.19–20). Cf. "The Haunter of the Dark": "bird-shunned shadows" (*CF* 3.465).

7–8 "The Colour out of Space" mentions deformed fauna and flora, and also the hopeless disappearance of the Gardner boys.

9–14 Cf. Henry Akeley's discussion with his mailman of the strange events that occurred at his farm in "The Whisperer in Darkness" (*CF* 2.499).

11 Aylesbury] A fictitious town of Lovecraft's invention, presumably near the fictional Dunwich, Massachusetts, first mentioned in "The Dunwich Horror." See also XXVI.11. The name is perhaps derived from Amesbury, a town in the far northeastern corner of the state, near Haverhill and Newburyport, and the late home of John Greenleaf Whittier. Lovecraft passed through Amesbury on several occasions, including in August 1927. There is a real town in England called Aylesbury.

14 The idea of a living hill is similar to an idea found in *CB 70*: "*Tone of extreme phantasy*[.] Man transformed to island or mountain."

VIII. The Port

"The Port" may have been suggested by the city of Marblehead, Mass. Lovecraft's initial visit to Marblehead on 17 December 1922 was one of the most moving experiences of his life.

> But not even from Salem did I go directly home; for whilst conversing with natives there, I had learnt of the neighbouring fishing port of *Marblehead*, whose antique quaintness was particularly recommended to me. Taking a stage-coach thither, I was presently borne into the most marvellous region I had ever dream'd of, & furnish'd with the most powerful single aesthetic impression I have receiv'd in years.
>
> Even now it is difficult for me to believe that Marblehead exists, save in some phantasticall dream. It is so contrary to everything usually observable in this age, & so exactly conform'd to the habitual fabrick of my nocturnal visions, that my whole visit partook of an aethereal character scarce compatible with reality. [. . .] The ground is very hilly, & the streets were made crooked & narrow, so that when finish'd, the town had gain'd much of the eccentrick aspect of such ancient Gothick towns as Nuremburg, in Bavaria, where the eye beholds small buildings heap'd about at all angles & all levels like an infant's blocks, & topp'd with a pleasing labyrinth of sharp gables, tall spires, & glittering vanes. [. . .] Over all the rest of the scene tower'd a hill on which the rude forefathers of the hamlet were laid to rest; & which was in consequence nam'd Old Burying Hill. [. . .]
>
> I came to Marblehead in the twilight, & gazed long upon its hoary magick. I threaded the tortuous, precipitous streets, some of which an horse can scarce climb, & in which two waggons cannot pass. I talked with old men & revell'd in old scenes, & climb'd pantingly over the crusted cliffs of snow to the windswept height where cold winds blew over desolate roofs & evil birds hovered over a bleak, deserted, frozen tarn. And atop all was the peak; Old Burying Hill. [. . .]
>
> Immemorial pinnacle of fabulous antiquity! As evening came I look'd down at the quiet village where the lights came out one by one; at the calm contemplative chimney-pots & antique gables silhouetted against the west; at the glimmering small-paned windows; at the silent & unillumined fort frowning formidably over the snug harbour. (11 January 1923, *RK* 200–01)

The visit described above was first worked into "The Festival" (see note on ll. 11–14), but the vivid impression stayed with Lovecraft for many years. Cf. *CB* 81: "Marblehead—dream—burying hill—evening—unreality."

1 Arkham] Arkham is the city invented by Lovecraft as a fictional equivalent to Salem. It was first mentioned in "The Picture in the House" and appears in many other stories of what Lovecraft called his "Arkham cycle."

2 Boynton Beach] There is a Boynton Beach in Florida, but Lovecraft surely did not intend the city in the poem to be the one in Florida. Lovecraft mentions a "Boynton" as among "parts of Quebeck Province near the Vermont border—the English-settled Eastern Townships—[that] have an Anglo-Saxon nomenclature and do not differ substantially in aspect and atmosphere from those of old New-England" (*CE* 4.176).

4 Innsmouth] Innsmouth, another of Lovecraft's fictional towns, is first mentioned in "Celephaïs," where it is situated in England. In "The Port" and all subsequent appearances, Innsmouth is a decaying seaport in Massachusetts—Lovecraft's fictional equivalent of Newburyport. In "The Shadow over Innsmouth," Lovecraft describes Innsmouth as being in a valley.

5–6 These lines are reminiscent of "The White Ship."

8–9 These lines anticipate the description in "The Shadow over Innsmouth" of a once flourishing center of trade that in the twentieth century is only a decayed, former seaport.

11–14 See Lovecraft to August Derleth: "What has haunted my dreams for nearly forty years is *a strange sense of adventurous expectancy* [cf. XXVIII] *connected with landscape & architecture & sky-effects.* I can see myself as a child of 2½ on the railway bridge at Auburndale, Mass., looking across & downward at the business part of the town, & feeling the imminence of some wonder which I could neither describe nor fully conceive—& there has never been a subsequent hour of my life when kindred sensations have been absent" (late December 1929, *ES* 1.237–38). Also cf. "The Festival": "Then beyond the hill's crest I saw Kingsport . . . with its ancient vanes and steeples, . . . [and] winter-whitened gables and gambrel roofs; fanlights and small-paned windows one by one gleaming out in the cold dusk" (*CF* 1.407; much of Lovecraft's letter of 11 January 1923 to Rheinhart Kleiner was used virtually verbatim in this description); and "The Music of Erich Zann": "I saw no city spread below, and no friendly lights gleaming from remembered streets, but only the blackness of space illimitable" (*CF* 1.289).

14 Cf. *CB* 155 (c. 1928): "Steepled town seen from afar at sunset—*does not light up at night.* Sail has been seen putting out to sea." Lovecraft acknowledged the influence of this entry with the late note "Fungi." Also cf. *CB* 203 (1934): "A return to a place under dreamlike, horrible, & only dimly comprehended circumstances. Death & decay reigning—town fails to light up at night—Revelation." In "The Shadow over Innsmouth," the narrator's escape from Innsmouth is illumined only by the moonlight.

IX. The Courtyard

Cf. *CB* 149 (c. 1928): "Evil alley or enclosed court in ancient city—Union or Milligan Pl." Lovecraft acknowledged the influence of the entry with the note "Fungi" in his notebook. The source for the sonnet was an actual place in New York City: "Loveman & I managed to escape unscathed from the hellish nocturnal Brooklyn court which we visited" (HPL to CAS, 14 April 1929 [*DS* 172]); and "[We] took McGrath out to see Union Place—that ancient and spectral courtyard which inspired one of my 'Fungi from Yuggoth.' It is just the same as ever—though we were there just too early to catch the most ghoulish note in its personality. It is . . . wholly hidden from the street proper—reached by an archway and long passage" (HPL to Lillian D. Clark, 8 July 1931 [*FFF* 937]). Lovecraft's aversion to New York is evident in "The Horror at Red Hook," "He," and "Cool Air," written in 1925–26 during his residence there.

Slum scenes, however, were not uncommon in Providence:

> I took a sunset-and-evening walk Thursday—a Machenesque Slum-and-Suburb pilgrimage in quest of mystery and horror—and found many things of striking and even of terrible novelty. It is astonishing what a wealth of hidden and tangled lanes and obscure, surprising quarters Providence possesses. A good three-quarters of my recent trip took place over territory my feet had never before trodden, and I found one monstrous and blasphemous neighbourhood whose existence I had never suspected—a region actually inhabited by degraded and quasi-human forms of life where I had always fancied there were merely factories and railway

yards. God, that frightful and cacodaemoniacal valley of grey tottering houses and black earth and choking smoke and nameless labyrinthine courts ſtraggling up ſteep coal-duſty hillsides without pavement, plan, or purpose! The houses are very tall and ancient and grey, with shaky clap-boards and shingles, and windows rheumy with unmentionable elder morbidities. Oozing out of various apertures and dragging themselves along the narrow lanes are shapeless forms of organic entity whose dead faces hint fiendishly of the rites and orgies and incantations in the hideous leaning synagogue whose wormy, unpainted boards hold ſtrange Eaſtern signs and unholy marks taken from the cabbala and the "Necronomicon". Awful things have been evoked in the pits under that accursed temple— one can read it in the puffy, malformed faces of the slug-like beings (half Jew and half nigger, apparently) which crawl about and wheeze in the acrid smoke which pours from passing trains . . . . or from secret nether altars. Ngrrrhh . . . . . I shall weave all this into a tale some day! Later phases of the walk gave me my firſt glimpse of the new local university of the Papiſts—Providence College, (a fine Gothick pile in a superb land-scape setting) and introduced me to a tangle of horrible and infinitely al-luring alleys of blackness in the Federal Hill Italian quarter—which the lateness of the hour prevented me from exploring. Truly, I have not yet examined so much as an eighth of my native town! (HPL to Frank Belk-nap Long, 23 April 1926, *SL* 2.43–44)

Cf. "He": "I was threading a series of detached courtyards; now accessible only through the unlighted hallways of intervening buildings, but once forming parts of a continuous network of piċturesque alleys. I had heard of them by vague rumour, and realised that they could not be upon any map of today; but the faċt that they were forgotten only endeared them to me, so that I had sought them with twice my usual eagerness" (*CF* 1.508). Olmſtead's room at the Gilman House in "The Shadow over Innsmouth" "overlooked a dingy courtyard" (*CF* 3.203). Although Lovecraft acknowl-edged the influence of the commonplace book entry on the sonnet, the incident that inspired "The Pigeon-Flyers" exerted some influence as well.

Firſt title: "Union Place."

1 Lovecraft describes the phenomenon called dejá vù, which he used in several other ſtories. Many of the dream cities in his fiċtion are familiar to

the characters in the stories, though they had never been to them ("Polaris," for example).

1–8 Cf. "He":

> For full three seconds I could glimpse that pandaemoniac sight, and in those seconds I saw a vista which will ever afterward torment me in dreams. I saw the heavens verminous with strange flying things, and beneath them a hellish black city of giant stone terraces with impious pyramids flung savagely to the moon, and devil-lights burning from unnumbered windows. And swarming loathsomely on aërial galleries I saw the yellow, squint-eyed people of that city, robed horribly in orange and red, and dancing insanely to the pounding of fevered kettle-drums, the clatter of obscene crotala, and the maniacal moaning of muted horns whose ceaseless dirges rose and fell undulantly like the waves of an unhallowed ocean of bitumen. (*CF* 1.514–15)

2–3 Cf. "The Cats": "Rabbles exotic to stranger-gods praying" (*AT* 72.11). Lovecraft often described the foreign-born denizens of New York City as "mongrels"; e.g., "The old New York is dead—this one is only a kennel of feverish mongrels" (HPL to Clark Ashton Smith, 18 February 1927, *DS* 121–22).

3 In New York, Lovecraft's neighbor in the room adjacent to his was a "Syrian [who] played eldritch and whining monotones on a strange bagpipe which made me dream ghoulish and incredible things" (HPL to Bernard Austin Dwyer, 26 March 1927, *MWM* 440).

4 In "The Horror at Red Hook," Lovecraft describes a series of underground tunnels and a "crypt beneath the dance-hall church" (*CF* 1.503) near the sea.

8 The narrator of "He" meets the man from the past in a dark courtyard.

12–14 Several of Lovecraft's stories concern reanimation of the dead, most notably "Herbert West—Reanimator" and *The Case of Charles Dexter Ward*. Cf. *CB* 152: "Autonomic nervous system and subconscious mind *do not reside in the head*. Have mad physician decapitate a man but keep him alive & subconsciously controlled."

Notes

Discarded lines:

It was the city I had known before,
Where mongrel millions, dragged from diſtant ſties
<And nightmare squalor ſtalks from door door
Down devious [?] ways of>
Of cringing filth, turn crafty night-black eyes
On alien gods that unknown lands adore.
It was the old, known way to where he dwelt—
He of ſtrange wisdom & ſtill ſtranger dream
I knew each lane where upper ſtories

X. The Pigeon-Flyers

Firſt title: "Hell's Kitchen."

The sport of pigeon-flying was popular in Europe and was introduced to the United States in the 1800s by immigrants. The flat-roofed tenements in New York proved to be ideal locations for playing the game. Two players launch their flocks, and the birds mix into a single group. The pigeons are trained to return with their own flock, but some birds become disoriented when the groups combine. The objeʄt of the game is to capture birds from the competitor's flock, as ſtrays inſtinʄtively join a flock, even a group of ſtrange birds. The sport is ſtill popular in all five boroughs of New York, although less than in Lovecraft's day. Cf. "[Chriſtmas Greeting]" to Annie E. P. Gamwell written in 1925 during Lovecraft's residence in New York:

> As when a pigeon loos'd in realms remote
> Takes inſtant wing, and seeks his native cote,
> So speed my blessings from a barb'rous clime
> To thee and Providence at Chriſtmas time. (*AT* 330)

R. Boerem implies that the city in IX and X is Innsmouth because of reference to Innsmouth in "The Port." But since the titles initially given the sonnets were "Union Place" and "Hell's Kitchen," the intended setting of both muſt be New York City. See Lovecraft to Auguſt Derleth (early January 1930, *ES* 242): "As for the sonnet you dislike—#10—I've had my doubts about that, too, because its appreciation depends upon a familiarity with the aʄtual cuſtoms of the 'Hell's Kitchen' slum in New York, where bonfire-building & pigeon-flying are the two leading recreations of youth. To one unacquainted with the region & its *mores,* the sonnet would inevitably have a tendency to seem pointless."

The poem was inspired by the death of Everett McNeil, a member of the Kalem Club, on 14 December 1929:

> I recall how he shewed Sonny [Frank Belknap Long] & me Hell's Kitchen—the first time either the Child or I ever saw it. Chasms of Hogarthian nightmare & odorous abomination—Baudelairian Satanism & cosmic terror—twisted, fantastic Nordic faces leering & grimacing beside night-lapping beacon-fires set to signal unholy planets—death brooding & gibbering in crypts & oozing out of the windows & cracks of unending bulging brick walls—sinister pigeon-breeders on filth-choked roofs sending birds of space out into black unknown gulfs with unrepeatable messages to the obscene, amorphous serpent-gods thereof [. . .] filth—odours—fantastic faces in bonfire-flares—swarming & morbid vitality. (HPL to James F. Morton, 18 December 1929, *JFM* 209)

> I recall when Mac first showed Belknap & me the nightmare horror of the Hell's Kitchen district (W. 49th St.) where he then lived—the seething filth of labyrinthine streets where grotesquely twisted faces leered in the glare of unclean bonfires lighted to signal the evil gods of alien worlds—the horrible rows of unending brick bulging with viscous horror & threatening to burst outward—the pigeon-breeders atop the foul tenements sending their birds of space outward into the void bearing messages for loathsome dark stars [. . .] (HPL to Zealia Brown Reed, 19 December 1929, *The Spirit of Revision* 165–66)

Lovecraft described New York to Morton as "a vision-metropolis; 'out of space, out of time' [from Poe's "Dream-Land"], & without linkage to the mundane, the material, & the perishable" (*JFM* 209). Another account of the visit to Hell's Kitchen is found in Lovecraft's letter to Maurice Moe of 18 January 1930 (pp. 171–72 herein).

1–3 See Lovecraft to Maurice W. Moe, 18 May 1922: "[Rheinhart] Klei[ner] [. . .] proceeded to lead us into the slums; with 'Chinatown' as an ulterior objective. My gawd—what a filthy dump! [. . .] damn me if I ever saw anything like the sprawling sty-atmosphere of N.Y.'s lower East Side. We walked—at my suggestion—in the middle of the street, for contact with the heterogeneous sidewalk denizens, spilled out of their bulging brick kennels as if by a spawning beyond the capacity of the places, was not by any means to be sought" (*MWM* 97). Writing to Robert E. Howard about old New York, Lovecraft stated:

> As for the lawless gangs of *old* New York—very differently organised and motivated from the economically-inspired gangs of today—they surely present some extremely dramatic situations. It must be remembered, however, that they were as definitely confined to an underworld as are their unworthy successors; and that no respectable New Yorker of the 1850's ever heard of them except through minor items in the press. Their battles all took place in slum areas given over to indescribable crime and squalor—areas into which no ordinary citizen ever set foot. In those days city slums were filthy and monstrous to a degree incredible in this generation. Nothing on this continent today is comparable in horror, disease, and general vileness to the Five Points or Cherry Street of the middle 19th century. Such districts were virtually fabulous and forbidden ground to the respectable people of their time—and even to this day not more than one New Yorker in a hundred has ever visited their relatively tame successors. Slumming was confined to a small and venturesome element of young bloods—for at that period no obviously respectable person was safe from assassination in the hell-roaring region east of the City Hall. You could probably have visited in New York for months in 1850 without coming across anybody—business-man, professor, clerk, mechanic, or any other normal type—who had ever been in contact with gangdom and its territory. Incidentally, it is only in the last few years that people outside New York have taken their present interest in the old gangs. This phase of local history was exceedingly obscure until modern gangdom revived the subject with the Rosenthal murder of 1912. (5 October 1932, *MF* 1.419–20)

Lovecraft knew of but probably did not read Herbert Asbury's *The Gangs of New York: An Informal History of the Underworld* (New York: Knopf, 1928).

5 As Lovecraft noted in his letter to August Derleth, in Hell's Kitchen bonfire building was one of "the leading recreations of youth."

8 The image of the rhythmic keeping of time is found in Donald Wandrei's "The Creatures," from *Sonnets of the Midnight Hours:* "And still those vast wings beat the sullen time" (*Sanctity and Sin* 124.6). See also "The Horror

at Red Hook": "Malone used to fancy he heard terrible cracked bass notes from a hidden organ far underground when the church ſtood empty and unlighted, whilſt all observers dreaded the shrieking and drumming which accompanied the visible services" (*CF* 1.488–89).

10 birds of space] The cover ſtory of *WT* for September 1928 was "The Bird of Space" by Everil Worrell. In July 1934 Lovecraft received a carving from Samuel Loveman, which he dubbed the "Bird of Space" (*FLB* 96).

Outside] The theme of "cosmic outsideness" became apparent in Lovecraft's writings in the summer of 1926, ſtarting with "The Call of Cthulhu," following his return to Providence from New York. See Lovecraft to Clark Ashton Smith, 7 [not 17] November 1930: "I want to know what ſtretches *Outside*, & to be able to *visit* all the gulfs & dimensions beyond Space & Time" (*DS* 263). It is perhaps beſt articulated in a letter to Farnsworth Wright of *WT*, written several months after the composition of "The Colour out of Space," Lovecraft's quintessential tale of cosmic outsideness:

> Now all my tales are based on the fundamental premise that common human laws and intereſts and emotions have no validity or significance in the vaſt cosmos-at-large. To me there is nothing but puerility in a tale in which the human form—and the local human passions and conditions and ſtandards—are depiĉted as native to other worlds or other universes. To achieve the essence of real externality, whether of time or space or dimension, one muſt forget that such things as organic life, good and evil, love and hate, and all such local attributes of a negligible and temporary race called mankind, have any exiſtence at all. Only the human scenes and charaĉters muſt have human qualities *These* muſt be handled with unsparing *realism*, (*not* catch-penny *romanticism*) but when we cross the line to the boundless and hideous unknown—the shadow-haunted *Outside*—we muſt remember to leave our humanity and terreſtrialism at the threshold. ("Letters to Farnsworth Wright" 7)

Likewise, Lovecraft's "Biographical Notice" of 1928, written for *The Beſt Short Stories of 1928 and the Yearbook of the American Short Story*, describes the focus of Lovecraft's literary efforts at the time to "tales of dream-life, ſtrange shadow, and cosmic 'outsideness', notwithſtanding sceptical rationalism of outlook and keen regard for the sciences" (*CE* 5.286).

Notes

Cf. "The Creatures" by Donald Wandrei: "Were they strange creatures from Outside that soon / Would seize their prey and seek their cosmic lair?" (*Sanctity and Sin* 124.7–8); "The Outpost": "The ancient Fishers from Outside" (*AT* 78.33); and "Winged Death": "a haunt or outpost of 'The Fishers from Outside' . . . and of the evil gods Tsadogwa and Clulu" (*CF* 4.396). Also see Lovecraft to F. Lee Baldwin, 27 March 1934 (*FLB* 54): "'The Thing from Outside' is exceedingly potent—I have read it 2 or 3 times, & have it in my file of the first year of *Amazing Stories*." "The Thing from—'Outside'" by George Allan England (1877–1936) appeared in *Amazing Stories* 1, No. 1 (April 1926): 67–91.

12 Thog] This is the only reference to *Thog* in Lovecraft's works and is not to be confused with the mountain *Thok* (XX.9), which was first mentioned in 1920 in "To a Dreamer" (*AT* 71.13). But see Lovecraft to R. H. Barlow, 1 September 1934: "Some night, in dreams, I hope to see a herd of [walla-roos] wighting thunderously over the plains of Thog!" (*OFF* 173).

XI. The Well

Cf. *CB* 143: "Strange well in Arkham country—water gives out (or was never struck—hole kept tightly covered by a stone ever since dug)—no bottom—shunned & feared—what lay beneath (either unholy temple or other very ancient thing, or great cave world)." Lovecraft acknowledged the influence of this entry with his note "Fungi—The Well" in his commonplace book. A "strange well" is the focus of the bizarre occurrences and subsequent madness in "The Colour out of Space."

About M. R. James's "The Treasure of Abbot Thomas," Lovecraft wrote in "Supernatural Horror in Literature": "But the crafty depositor had set a guardian over that treasure, and something in the black well twines its arms around the searcher's neck in such a manner that the quest is abandoned, and a clergyman sent for. . . . finally the cleric observes a curious toad-like carving on the ancient well-head, with the Latin motto '*Depositum custodi*—keep that which is committed to thee'" (*CE* 2.124–25).

1 Atwood] In *At the Mountains of Madness* a professor from the physics department of Miskatonic University on the expedition to Antarctica is

named Atwood. There is a Rev. Silas Atwood in "The Horror in the Burying Ground."

6 county farm] I.e., a town farm or poor farm. Poor farms were county- or town-run residences where paupers (mainly elderly and disabled people) were supported at public expense. Such farms were common in the United States in the 19th and early 20th centuries. The farms fell out of use after the Social Security Act (1935) took effect, most disappearing by about 1950. The Dexter Asylum, built in 1828, was a poor farm on the East Side of Providence. It housed poor, elderly, and mentally ill residents who could not otherwise care for themselves. In 1957 it was sold to Brown University and demolished to make way for athletic fields and buildings. It is unknown if Lovecraft meant the "county farm" to be identical to the "Aylesbury town farm" in XXVI.11.

9–14 These lines recall the inspection of Nahum Gardner's well in "The Colour out of Space." Although the well was emptied of water, it was found that a "wooden shaft [could be sunk] to any depth in the mud of the floor without meeting any solid obstruction" (*CF* 2.390).

14 Cf. "The Horror at Red Hook": "the canal was observed to sink into a well too deep for dredging" (*CF* 1.503).

Discarded lines:

> XI.
> Farmer Seth Atwood was past eighty when
> He tried to sink that well beside his door;
> We laughed to see the old \<man\> fool bore & bore
> With only Tom & Eb as extra men.
> They snickered too, till one day they were gone,
> And Seth allowed he'd dug about enough.
> No water—this rock soil was tarnal stuff,
> So 'twould be foolish to keep diggin' on.
>
> \<We never saw\> Young Tom & Eb dropped wholly out of sight;
> But Seth grew spry & often used to grin
> When we asked why he bricked the well-head in—
> \<After he shot himself we moved the stone\>

Notes

And then he went & shot himself one night.
We wrecked the bricks—& in that black hole found
Just spikes

[new line 5] They snickered too, till old Seth had to say
He'd dug enough—this soil was dirty as Tophet—
And 'twould be sin to squander work & profit.
But Tom & Eb dropped out of sight to stay.

Seth bricked the well-head up & used to grin
When we asked why, & then one night toward May
He shot himself, & all the folks trooped in
The stony yard to rip the bricks away.
Spike steps down a deep pit were all they found—
But 'twas too deep for any line to sound!

XII. The Howler

Cf. *CB* 117: "A secret living thing kept & fed in an old house"; and 118: "Something seen at oriel window of forbidden room in ancient manor house." The entries date to 1923, around the time Lovecraft wrote "The Unnamable."

1 In the opening paragraph of "The Dunwich Horror," it is said that a person reaches Dunwich by taking the "wrong fork at the junction of the Aylesbury pike just beyond Dean's Corners" (*CF* 2.417).

Briggs' Hill] The only mention in Lovecraft. Fictitious, but see Lovecraft to Lillian D. Clark, 16–17 February 1926 (*LFF* 563): "The other Attleboro–Taunton line—the one that passed Briggs' Corners & the sanitarium & had a branch to Pawtucket—was abandoned & torn up years ago."

2 highroad] A main road or highway (chiefly British).

Zoar] A town in northwestern Massachusetts near the Vermont border; in the Bible, the city in Egypt where Lot took refuge from the destruction of Sodom (Gen. 13:10). Lovecraft traveled near or through it in May 1929 (*ET* 71–72). Cf. "[On Phillips Gamwell]": "On Zoar's proud height, of heav'n itself a part, / Gamwell sees all, without the need of art!" (*AT* 427.9–10).

3 A witch named Goody Fowler is mentioned in "The Silver Key" and "Through the Gates of the Silver Key," presumably the same person. Why she was hanged is never said. When Lovecraft was exploring Danvers, Mass.—the original Salem-Village—he sought to inspect the Capt. Samuel Fowler house (1809), as he related to Alfred Galpin and Frank Belknap Long on 1 May 1923:

> Inform'd by the sign that this was the Capt. Samuel Fowler house, built 1809, accessible for eightpence, and the property of the Society for the Preservation of New-England Antiquities, I loudly sounded the knocker and awaited developments. [. . .]
>
> My summons was answer'd simultaneously by two of the most pitiful and decrepit-looking persons imaginable—hideous old women more sinister than the witches of 1692, and certainly not under 80. For a moment I believ'd them to be Salem witches in truth; for the peculiarly sardonick face of one of them, with furtive eyes, sneering lips, and a conspicuously undershot lower jaw, intensify'd the impression produc'd by their incredible age and gauntness, and the utterly nondescript bundles of brownish rags which form'd their attire. The "ell" in which they dwelt was in a state of indescribable squalor; with heaps of rags, books, cooking utensils, and the like on every hand. [. . .] If, however, their weird aspect and hideous squalor were sinister; what can one say of the *contrast* involv'd when the guttural salutation of the speaker became intelligible? For despite the omnipresent evidences of a slatternly decadence beyond words, this ancient witch was mumbling forth a courtly and aristocratick welcome in language and accents beyond question bespeaking the gentlest birth and proudest cultivation! The witch apologised for the unfavourable conditions prevailing, and lamented that she had not heard my knocking at the front door of the mansion proper. [. . .] These tatter'd ancients were the Misses Fowler, own granddaughters of the proud seafarer and fighter who in his dashing prime had built that house for the comfort, dignity, and splendour of his descendants. Short-sighted man! Had he but foreseen the depths to which those descendants wou'd be driven! (*Letters to Alfred Galpin* 139)

Of course, Adelaide Fowler (1843–1934) and Sarah P. Fowler (1853–1930) were born on the order of a century and a half after the demise of the fictional character. The Salem witch trials occurred in 1692. Lovecraft mentions other witches in "Pickman's Model" and "The Dreams in the

Witch House," and Robert Blake's unfinished witch novel in "The Haunter of the Dark."

6 Cf. "The Colour out of Space": "On the gentler slopes there are farms, ancient and rocky, with squat, moss-coated cottages brooding eternally over old New England secrets in the lee of great ledges" (*CF* 2.367).

10–12 Cf. "The Unnamable": "furtive tales of things with a blemished eye seen at windows in the night" (*CF* 1.401); and "The Thing on the Door-step": "at one of Edward's library windows, she had glimpsed a hastily withdrawn face—a face whose expression of pain, defeat, and wistful hopelessness was poignant beyond description" (*CF* 3.335). In "The Unnamable," Randolph Carter is the author of a story titled "The Attic Window." In "The Colour out of Space," Nabby Gardner is confined to the attic when she goes insane.

14 The creature described here may have suggested Brown Jenkin in "The Dreams in the Witch House": "in 1692 no less than eleven persons had testified to glimpsing it. . . . [I]t had long hair and the shape of a rat, but . . . its sharp-toothed bearded face was evilly human while its paws were like tiny human hands" (*CF* 3.236).

XIII. Hesperia

Title: Hesperia was "the land to the west"; to the Greeks it was Italy, to the Romans it was Spain or regions beyond. It derives from the word *Hesperus,* the evening star (cf. XXXV), the planet Venus in the evening. Lovecraft had circulated a "manuscript magazine" in Great Britain between 1918 and 1921 titled *Hesperia.* Cf. "Poetry and the Gods": "sleeping the sleep and dreaming the dreams of Gods in lotos-filled Hesperian gardens beyond the golden sunset" (*CF* 4.22).

5 Cf. "The East India Brick Row": "With hinted wonders from a fire-lashed west" (*AT* 308.12).

7 sphinxes] Cf. *The Dream-Quest of Unknown Kadath:* "an avenue of un-natural sphinxes leading to what was once a public square" (*CF* 2.121); and *The Case of Charles Dexter Ward:* "People who smelled [odours from Ward's laboratory] had a tendency to glimpse momentary mirages of enormous

viStas, with Strange hills or endless avenues of sphinxes and hippogriffs Stretching off into infinite diStance" (*CF* 2.287). Steven J. Mariconda sug-geSts that this image may have been inspired by the Avenue of Sphinxes of the Temple of Ammon.

11 river Time] Cf. XXIII.2: "Time's Stream."

14 Lovecraft's Stories and letters contain numerous references to cities whose Streets have never been touched by human feet—in dreamlands, in ancient cities discovered for the firSt time in the twentieth century, in the prehiStoric cities unearthed in *At the Mountains of Madness* and "The Shadow out of Time," and even Streets never explored previously by him— a conceit that obviously appealed to him. See, e.g., "The Haunter of the Dark": "Nowhere could he find any of the objeCts he had seen from afar; so that once more he half fancied that the Federal Hill of that diStant view was a dream-world never to be trod by living human feet" (*CF* 3.455).

XIV. Star-Winds

Title: Cf. "Nyarlathotep": "charnel winds that brush the pallid Stars and make them flicker low" (*CF* 1.205); "The Crawling Chaos": "a fragrant breeze which blew not from the earth but from the golden nebulae" (*CF* 4.35); "The Hound": "Madness rides the Star-wind" (*CF* 1.348); "Hyp-nos": "winds from unknown spaces whirled us irresiStibly into limitless vacua beyond all thought and entity" (*CF* 1.328); and "The Colour out of Space": "all about was a mounting wind which seemed to sweep down in black, frore guSts from interStellar space" (*CF* 2.396).

7 geometries of outer space] Cf. "The Call of Cthulhu": "Wilcox had told me of his awful dreams. He had said that the *geometry* of the dream-place he saw was abnormal, non-Euclidean, and loathsomely redolent of spheres and dimensions apart from ours" (*CF* 2.51); *At the Mountains of Madness:* "There were geometrical forms for which an Euclid could scarcely find a name . . ." (*CF* 3.80); and "Through the Gates of the Silver Key": "alien and incomprehensible designs and disposed according to the laws of some un-known, inverse geometry" (*CF* 3.290).

8 Fomalhaut] A Star of the firSt magnitude in the conStellation Piscis Aus-tralis, the Southern Fish. In "The September Heavens," Lovecraft observed:

"this group is so far south it [Fomalhaut] is not well seen in our latitude, but to an observer in Florida or Texas it is indeed a beautiful sight" (*CE* 3.47). Lovecraft, of course, made this comment years before he had been to Florida, where he could see the star to best advantage. Cf. *The Dream-Quest of Unknown Kadath:* "not only had no man ever been to unknown Kadath, but no man ever had suspected in what part of space it may lie; whether it be in the dreamlands around our world, or in those surrounding some unguessed companion of Fomalhaut or Aldebaran" (*CF* 2.100).

9 moonstruck] Affected by insanity (from the belief that the moon [luna] caused insanity [lunacy]). Cf. "Supernatural Horror in Literature": "unholy dimensions which only the dead and the moonstruck can glimpse" (*CE* 2.84).

10 what fungi sprout in Yuggoth] See the introductory note under the series title and the note on IV.12. Cf. "Through the Gates of the Silver Key": "He saw Kynarth and Yuggoth on the rim, passed close to Neptune and glimpsed the hellish white fungi that spot it, learned an untellable secret from the close-glimpsed mists of Jupiter and saw the horror on one of the satellites, and gazed at the Cyclopean ruins that sprawl over Mars' ruddy disc" (*CF* 3.315).

11 Nithon] This constitutes the only mention of *Nithon* in Lovecraft's works. Nithon is a planet, and thus different from "Nython" in "Through the Gates of the Silver Key," described there as a "triple star." S. T. Joshi suggests that the word may be derived from the Greek νήθω, to spin ("Lovecraft's Other Planets" 4).

Discarded lines:

The <mad> dead leaves rush in queer fantastic whorls,
Heeding geometries of <other stars> distant space,
And chimney-smoke ascends in alien curls

XV. Antarktos

Ἄρκτός is Greek for *bear,* and refers to the constellation Ursa Major and also the Pole Star.

Title: From the Greek ἀνταρκτικός (adjective)—opposite the north; thus, the south polar region, or Antarctica, the setting of *At the Mountains of Madness.* This constitutes the only mention of *Antarktos* in Lovecraft's works. But see *The Dream-Quest of Unknown Kadath:* "The zoogs . . . [could not] say whether the cold waste is in our dream-world or in another" (*CF* 2.103). Cf. Lovecraft to Elizabeth Toldridge, 25 October 1929: "Lost Arctic & Antarctic civilisations form a fascinating idea to me–I used it once in 'Polaris', & expect to use it again more than once" (*ET* 113). Note that "Antarktos" appeared in the same issue of *WT* (November 1930) as "A Million Years After," by Katherine Metcalf Roof. Lovecraft found Roof's story so poor that he resolved to write his own dinosaur egg story; cf. *CB* 169: "What hatches from primordial egg." His sonnet, his general interest in Antarctica, and the desire to write a truly original dinosaur egg story collectively influenced the composition of *At the Mountains of Madness,* begun the following January.

1 Cf. *CB* 127: "Ancient & unknown ruins—strange & immortal bird who SPEAKS in a language horrifying & revelatory to the explorers." In Poe's *Narrative of Arthur Gordon Pym of Nantucket* and Lovecraft's *At the Mountains of Madness,* a speaking bird cries *"Tekeli-li!"*

1–4 These lines anticipate the eroded mountain ramparts in Antarctica, described throughout *At the Mountains of Madness* as being like the paintings of Nicholas Roerich.

2 black cone] Cf. *The Dream-Quest of Unknown Kadath:* "the rugged conical mass" (*CF* 2.200); and *At the Mountains of Madness:* "the jagged line of witch-like cones" (*CF* 3.50). Perhaps Lovecraft alludes to the volcano Mt. Erebus in Antarctica.

8 Elder Ones] Cf. XXVII.7; also "The Strange High House in the Mist": "the dim first age of chaos before the gods or even the Elder Ones were born" (*CF* 2.93). The term is also used in *The Dream-Quest of Unknown Kadath* in reference to some unspecified entities. In *At the Mountains of Madness,* Antarctica once was populated by a race known as the Old Ones (at times referred to as "Elder Things").

10 mound] At the time Lovecraft was writing *Fungi from Yuggoth*, he was ghostwriting "The Mound" for Zealia Bishop. The mound in this sonnet, however, is not manmade.

12 mile-deep ice-shroud] Cf. *At the Mountains of Madness:* "Our borings, of varying depth according to the promise held out by the upper soil or rock, were to be confined to exposed or nearly exposed land surfaces—these inevitably being slopes and ridges because of the mile or two-mile thickness of solid ice overlying the lower levels" (*CF* 3.14–15).

14 Cf. *At the Mountains of Madness:* "we could see beneath certain transparent parts of the ice-sheet" (*CF* 3.80); and "'the eyes in darkness'" (*CF* 3.157).

Discarded lines:

Amid the polar waste its monstrous girth
Looms like a black hill grown from the abyss
_____ no stone of this non-transient earth,

XVI. The Window

Cf. *CB* 195: "Pane of peculiar-looking glass from a ruined monastery reputed to have harboured devil-worship set up in modern house at edge of wild country. Landscape looks vaguely & unplaceably *wrong* through it. It has some unknown time-distorting quality, & comes from a primal lost *civilisation.* Finally, hideous things in other world seen through it." The octave seems to describe Lovecraft's own boyhood: "I guess I told you how much time I spent in the attic of my old home—with a candle in a sinister windowless room, where I found all the brown-backed 18th century volumes which had been banished from the more elegant shelves downstairs" (HPL to Henry Kuttner, 15 October 1936, *CLM* 253). In the 1930s, Lovecraft wrote notes for a possible story that contain a reference to a window to another dimension:

> Is lens, prism, or mirror reflecting vision from other dimension or dimensions—time or space. Or rather, reflecting obscure rays not of vision but operating on vestigial and forgotten extra senses. Constructed by outside

Entities in effort to inspect human world—or rather, const. by elder wizard under their direction.

Outer beings peer through it. Influence humans by opening up other senses and dimension-perceptions possibly including hereditary memory. Explains odd dreams of strange horror. Also works through dreams. ("[The Rose Window]," *CE* 5.254)

1–2 Cf. Lovecraft's description in a letter to Bernard Austin Dwyer, 26 March 1927, of his apartment in New York City at 169 Clinton Street: "I never quite learned the exact topography of that rambling and enormous house. [. . .] there were wings and corridors I never traversed; doors to rear and abutting halls and stairways that I never saw opened. I know there were rooms above ground without windows" (*MWM* 441).

4 Cf. Lovecraft's notes for an uncompleted story (now known as "The Round Tower"): "S. of Arkham is cylindrical tower of stone with conical roof—perhaps 12 feet across & 20 ft. high. There has been a great arched opening quarter way up, but it is sealed up with masonry" (*CE* 5.253). There was a similar structure in Newport, R.I., known as The Newport Tower (also Round Tower) located in Touro Park.

5 dream-plagued childhood] Cf. note on XX.

9–14 Recall the frightened workmen who must clear out Walter Gilman's room in "The Dreams in the Witch House."

11–12 These lines recall the discovery of the hidden crypt in "The Rats in the Walls" and the discovery and unveiling of the portrait of Joseph Curwen in *The Case of Charles Dexter Ward*.

14 In "The Haunter of the Dark," the Shining Trapezohedron is a metaphorical "window on all time and space [that] was fashioned on dark Yuggoth" (*CF* 3.467). The window in this poem is a gateway to another realm.

Discarded lines:

All his short life he saw the smoke-like line
On the plain's rim that meant the far-off hills,
And from the city walls would

Always at daylight's end the phantom hung

Notes

Glimmering above the western roof-line's edge;
Low, level plains where faintly-waving sedge
Rose along creeks from a great salt bay flung

XVII. A Memory

"A Memory" and "The Gardens of Yin" derive from a single paragraph in "Celephaïs." See below.

Title: Lovecraft originally had titled this sonnet "Recognition" and undoubtedly changed it when he realized he had used the title for sonnet IV.

1–8 Cf. "Celephaïs": "One night [Kuranes] went flying over dark mountains where there were faint, lone campfires at great distances apart, and strange, shaggy herds with tinkling bells on the leaders; and in the wildest part of this hilly country, so remote that few men could ever have seen it, he found a hideously ancient wall or causeway of stone zigzagging along the ridges and valleys; too gigantic ever to have risen by human hands, and of such a length that neither end of it could be seen" (*CF* 1.188).

1 table-lands] Plateaus. Cf. *The Dream-Quest of Unknown Kadath:* "finally they came to a windswept table-land which seemed the very roof of a blasted and tenantless world" (*CF* 2.172); and *At the Mountains of Madness:* "Here, on a hellishly ancient table-land fully 20,000 feet high, and in a climate deadly to habitation since a pre-human age not less than 500,000 years ago, there stretched nearly to the vision's limit a tangle of orderly stone which only the desperation of mental self-defence could possibly attribute to any but a conscious and artificial cause" (*CF* 3.71).

3 Cf. *The Dream-Quest of Unknown Kadath:* "Around the feeble fires dark forms were dancing" (*CF* 2.171).

4 tinkling bells] Cf. *The Dream-Quest of Unknown Kadath:* "for six days they rode with tinkling bells on the smooth road beside the Skai" (*CF* 2.108).

6 The wall referred to in this poem and XVIII (and initially in "Celephaïs") is the Great Wall of China.

13–14 Cf. "The Festival": "Presently the old man drew back his hood and pointed to the family resemblance in his face. . . . [A sudden] motion dislodged the waxen mask from what should have been his head. . . . I flung myself into the oily underground river . . . before the madness of my screams could bring down upon me all the charnel legions these pest-gulfs might conceal" (*CF* 1.415–16); *The Dream-Quest of Unknown Kadath:* "priests in the masked and hooded columns [who] are not human priests" (*CF* 2.163); and "The Thing on the Doorstep": "The Hooded Thing" (*CF* 3.338).

14 Cf. VII.8: "whose kin had ceased to hope."

XVIII. The Gardens of Yin

Lovecraft had written in 1917 of a garden sometimes seen in dream in his poem "A Garden."

Title: This constitutes the only mention of *Yin* in Lovecraft's works; but note "the vaults of Zin" in *The Dream-Quest of Unknown Kadath. Yin* is a place name of Lovecraft's invention and as such bears no relation to the principle of yin/yang of Chinese philosophy, despite the sonnet's general Oriental tone. See Lovecraft to Elizabeth Toldridge, 25 March 1933: "My admiration of Japanese art—dating from the days when my infant eyes rested upon various screens, fans, & bits of pottery at the old home—has always been prodigiously keen" (*ET* 232). Yin—indeed the very sonnet— may derive from *Yian* in Robert W. Chambers's "The Maker of Moons." For example, "Oh yes. He made it also in Yian and I loved to watch the sparks at night whirling like golden bees. Yian is lovely,—if it is all like our garden and the gardens around. I can see the thousand bridges from my garden and the white mountain beyond—" (121).

In May 1930, Lovecraft was impressed by a visit to Maymont Park in Richmond, Virginia: "what a world of delirious, unpredictable loveliness & dreamlike enchantment!! Poe's 'Domain of Arnheim' and 'Island of the Fay' all rolled into one . . . . with my own 'Gardens of Yin' added for good measure! [. . .] *I have actually found the garden of my earliest dreams* (HPL to James F. Morton, 15 May 1930, *JFM* 230). Other walled gardens are found in "Ex Oblivione," "What the Moon Brings," and most especially *The Dream-Quest of Unknown Kadath* (*CF* 2.163).

1–8 Cf. "Celephaïs":

> Beyond that wall in the grey dawn he came to a land of quaint gardens and cherry trees, and when the sun rose he beheld such beauty of red and white flowers, green foliage and lawns, white paths, diamond brooks, blue lakelets, carven bridges, and red-roofed pagodas, that he for a moment forgot Celephaïs in sheer delight. But he remembered it again when he walked down a white path toward a red-roofed pagoda, and would have questioned the people of that land about it, had he not found that there were no people there, but only birds and bees and butterflies. (*CF* 1.188–89)

Note the titles of Ambrose Bierce's story "Beyond the Wall" (in *Can Such Things Be?*), and Lovecraft's own "Beyond the Wall of Sleep," a story about the dream experience: "Whilst the greater number of our nocturnal visions are perhaps no more than faint and fantastic reflections of our waking experiences . . . there are still a certain remainder whose immundane and ethereal character permits of no ordinary interpretation, and whose vaguely exciting and disquieting effect suggests possible minute glimpses into a sphere of mental existence no less important than physical life, yet separated from that life by an all but impassable barrier. (*CF* 1.71–2).

14 gate] See *OED*, s.v. *Gate*: "5. *fig.* A means of entrance or exit."

Discarded lines:

There would be gardens in the \<low, warm lands\> warm, low valley
Beyond that ancient well whose moss-thick stones
Reached almost to the sky, & magically
Drew the

A thousand dreams had shewn that scene to me
So that I could have found ___

XIX. The Bells

Cf. *CB* 39: "*Sounds*—possibly musical—heard in the night from other worlds or realms of being." Poe also wrote a poem titled "The Bells," and Lovecraft wrote the poem "Bells" in 1919. Cf. "The Bells" from Donald Wandrei's *Sonnets of the Midnight Hours*. (The date of composition of this sonnet is unknown; it did not appear in *WT*.)

See Docherty, Searles, and Faig: "Lovecraft would have loved the legend connected with the missing bells of St. Symphorian in Forrabury [Cornwall]. Three bells ordered by William, Lord of Bottreaux Castle, to ward off the plague were lost when a sudden storm arose in the nearby harbor. The lord and his wife duly perished of the plague, but even today residents of Boscastle say that the ghostly peal of the lost bells can be heard whenever a storm is brewing" (9). See also Lovecraft to Elizabeth Toldridge, 1 October 1929: "America never had this bit of colour [i.e., carillons], for Puritan steeples generally boasted only a single bell. Still—even those unvarying peals sound highly picturesque & attractive across a rural valley through the haze of summer or over the crisp Christmas snows" (*ET* 108).

1–4 Cf. "The Strange High House in the Mist": "the solemn bells of buoys tolled free in the aether of faery" (*CF* 2.87); and "The Book": "There were chimes that came every now and then from distant belfries" (p. 236).

3 In "The Haunter of the Dark," Robert Blake searches with some difficulty for a church steeple that he observed some distance from his dwelling place.

11 Cf. "Bells":

> I hear the bells—the mocking, cursed bells
>> That wake dim memories to haunt and chill;
> Ringing and ringing o'er a thousand hells—
>> Fiends of the Night—why can ye not be still? (*AT* 69.41–44)

12 Cf. "The Haunter of the Dark": "He saw towers and walls in nighted depths under the sea, and vortices of space where wisps of black mist floated before thin shimmerings of cold purple haze" (*CF* 3.465).

13–14 The bells tolling in towers under the sea evoke the similarly submerged towers in Poe's "The City in the Sea."

Discarded lines:

Of Innsmouth, where above a churchyard's dead
The well-remembered village steeple
                  spire broods
Fearful St. Toad's, amidst the night[mare?]
                in streets of walking dead,

Of sea-washed Innsmouth, where

Of quiet Innsmouth, by whose ancient shore
A well-remembered tower once raised its head.

Till one bleak autumn night besides my bed
The glutinous tones of the familiar dead
Lifted the veil & crazed me with recalling.
Now when they sing I know my soul must

XX. Night-Gaunts

Title: Lovecraft coined the term "night-gaunts" when he was five years old. The death of his grandmother Robie Alzada (Place) Phillips on 26 January 1896 provoked

> nightmares of the most hideous description, peopled with *things* which I called "night-gaunts" [. . .] I used to draw them after waking (perhaps the idea of these figures came from an edition de luxe of "Paradise Lost" with illustrations by Doré, which I discovered one day in the east parlour). In dreams they were wont to whirl me through space at a sickening rate of speed, the while fretting & impaling me with their detestable tridents. (HPL to Rheinhart Kleiner, 16 November 1916, *RK* 66)

> [They] used to snatch me up by the stomach [. . .] and carry me off through infinite leagues of black air over the towers of dead and horrible cities. They would finally get into a grey void where I could see the needle-like pinnacles of enormous mountains miles below. Then they would let drop—and as I gained momentum in my Icarus-like plunge I would start awake in such a panic that I hated to think of sleeping again. The "night-gaunts" were black, lean, rubbery things with bared, barbed tails, bat-wings and *no faces at all.* [. . .] They had no voices, and their only form of real torture was their habit of tickling my stomach [. . .] before snatching me up and swooping away with me. I sometimes had the vague notion that they lived in the black burrows honeycombing the pinnacle of some incredibly high mountains somewhere. They seemed to come in flocks of 25 or 50, and would sometimes fling me one to the other. Night after night I dreamed the same horror with only minor variants—but I never struck those hideous mountain peaks before waking. (HPL to Virgil Finlay, 24 October 1936, *SL* 5.335)

The poem is a retelling of Randolph Carter's capture by the night-gaunts in *The Dream-Quest of Unknown Kadath*. Similar creatures made their appearances in "Celephaïs": "laughing winged things that seemed to mock the dreamers of all the worlds (*CF* 1.186); "The Rats in the Walls": "a legion of bat-winged devils" (*CF* 1.380); "He": "I saw a vista which will ever afterward torment me in dreams. I saw the heavens verminous with strange flying things, and beneath them a hellish black city of giant stone terraces with impious pyramids flung savagely to the moon" (*CF* 1.514); "Pickman's Model": "The texture of the majority was a kind of unpleasant rubberiness" (*CF* 2.64); and "The Call of Cthulhu": "Black Winged Ones" (*CF* 2.38) and "the green, bat-winged mocking imps of Tartarus" (*CF* 2.55). Cf. n. 6 in Appendix A.

2 Cf. "The Horror in the Museum": "a lean, rubbery night-gaunt" (*CF* 4.436). Of course, no reader of *WT* had any idea what the ostensible author (Hazel Heald) meant by this, because Lovecraft's *The Dream-Quest of Unknown Kadath* was unpublished at the time, and the sonnet "Night-Gaunts" had appeared only in the *Providence Journal*.

4 bifid] Divided into two equal parts by a median cleft.

8 grey world] Yuggoth is a "grey world" (IV.11–12).

9 Thok] There is a dragon named Thok in Dunsany's "The Fortress Unvanquishable, Save for Sacnoth" (in *The Sword of Welleran*). Cf. "To a Dreamer": "I, too, have known the peaks of Thok" (*AT* 71.13); *The Dream-Quest of Unknown Kadath*: "he saw faint lines of grey and ominous pinnacles which he knew must be the fabled Peaks of Thok" (*CF* 2.131); and "The Book": "the needle-like pinnacles of unknown mountains miles below me" (p. 237).

12 shoggoths] This constitutes the first mention of *shoggoths* in Lovecraft's works, first appearing in print in the *Providence Journal* in March 1930. Of course, the readers of the *Journal* had no idea what Lovecraft was referring to, and perhaps neither did he. He mentions shoggoths only tangentially in headings to letters to Clark Ashton Smith in 1930, but finally describes them in *At the Mountains of Madness* as "multicellular protoplasmic masses capable of moulding their tissues into all sorts of temporary organs under

hypnotic influence" (*CF* 3.95). In "The Shadow over Innsmouth," Zadok Allen cryptically asks the narrator "ever hear tell of a *shoggoth?*" (*CF* 3.200), and in "The Thing on the Doorstep," Edward Pickman Derby mentions "The pit of the shoggoths! . . . the unholy pit where the black realm begins and the watcher guards the gate" (*CF* 3.337–38). It was not until early 1936 that readers learned just what shoggoths are.

13–14 See Lovecraft to Rheinhart Kleiner, 16 November 1916: "when half asleep & drifting vaguely along over a sea of childhood thoughts, I feel a thrill of fear—something like that in Mrs. Jordan's poem 'The Pool'—& instinctively *struggle to keep awake*. That was my one prayer back in '96— each night—to *keep awake* & ward off the night-gaunts!" (*RK* 66). Cf. "The Pool" by Winifred Virginia Jordan:

> But Oh! sometimes in dream I hear
>   A whisper, then a torrent's roar;
> The shriek of winds, the belch of fear,
>   That I have known somewhere before!
>   (*Conservative* 2, No. 3 [October 1916]: [7])

XXI. Nyarlathotep

R. H. Barlow observed that "Azathoth—Nyarlathotep was based on a dream-name (*OFF* 404).

Title: Lovecraft did not so much conceive of Nyarlathotep as *dream* of him; see Lovecraft's celebrated letter to Rheinhart Kleiner of 14 December 1920 (*RK* 174–75). The description of Lovecraft's famous dream, particularly the "horrible—possibly prophetic—cinema reel" seems significant in the composition of this sonnet and the description of the future events. This sonnet is a condensed retelling of the prose poem, "Nyarlathotep," written immediately after Lovecraft's dream. About Nyarlathotep himself, Lovecraft had once written:

> And it was then that Nyarlathotep came out of Egypt. Who he was, none could tell, but he was of the old native blood and looked like a Pharaoh. The fellahin knelt when they saw him, yet could not say why. He said he had risen up out of the blackness of twenty-seven centuries, and that he had heard messages from places not on this planet. Into the lands of

civilisation came Nyarlathotep, swarthy, slender, and sinister, always buying strange instruments of glass and metal and combining them into instruments yet stranger. He spoke much of the sciences—of electricity and psychology—and gave exhibitions of power which sent his spectators away speechless, yet which swelled his fame to exceeding magnitude. (*CF* 1.203)

In "The Shadow out of Time," Nathaniel Wingate Peaslee talked with [the mind] "of Khephnes, an Egyptian of the 14th Dynasty who told me the hideous secret of Nyarlathotep" (*CF* 3.399).

There are numerous other references to Nyarlathotep in Lovecraft's stories, most notably in *The Dream-Quest of Unknown Kadath,* "The Whisperer in Darkness," and "The Haunter of the Dark." The following, from "The Dreams in the Witch House," describes Nyarlathotep analogously to the description here: "Old legends are hazy and ambiguous, and in historic times all attempts at crossing forbidden gaps seem complicated by strange and terrible alliances with beings and messengers from outside. There was the immemorial figure of the deputy or messenger of hidden and terrible powers—the 'Black Man' of the witch-cult, and the 'Nyarlathotep' of the "'Necronomicon'" (*CF* 3.260).

Several items listed in Appendix A seem to have some bearing on the poem, such as nn. 7, 16, 17, and 32. The name *Nyarlathotep* first appeared in print in the *United Amateur* for November 1920, when Lovecraft's prose poem was published. Nyarlathotep is mentioned quite offhandedly in "The Rats in the Walls" in *WT* (March 1924), but more prominently in "The Whisperer in Darkness," for in that story Nyarlathotep apparently assumes the bodily identity of Henry Wentworth Akeley. Lovecraft refers to Nyarlathotep repeatedly as "the crawling chaos," a conceit first put forth in the prose poem "Nyarlathotep." Although Nyarlathotep is the subject of this sonnet, Lovecraft did not strike n. 32, "Crawling Chaos," his epithet, from his list of ideas for poems.

Dunsany's "The Sorrow of Search" (in *Time and the Gods*) refers to a Mynarthitep (see also note on XXXII.6).

2 fellahs] A *fellah* is a peasant in Arabic-speaking countries; in English, it is especially applied to one in Egypt. Lovecraft knew the preferred plural form, *fellaheen* (cf. *JVS* 143) or fellahin as in "Nyarlathotep" (*CF* 1.203). The three-syllable plural would not scan properly here and so he used *fellahs* instead.

8–14 Robert Bloch used this image in the conclusion of his story "The Shadow from the Steeple" (1950), where these lines are quoted, and also in his novel *Strange Eons* (1978).

9 Cf. "The Nightmare Lake":

> Then sank the lake within its bed,
> Suck'd down to caverns of the dead,
> Till from the reeking, new-stript earth
> Curl'd foetid fumes of noisome birth. (*AT* 70.53–56)

9–12 Cf. "Dagon": "I dream of a day when they may rise above the billows to drag down in their reeking talons the remnants of puny, war-exhausted mankind—of a day when the land shall sink, and the dark ocean floor shall ascend amidst universal pandemonium" (*CF* 1.58); and "The Call of Cthulhu": "Loathsomeness waits and dreams in the deep, and decay spreads over the tottering cities of men" (*CF* 2.55).

13–14 A similar concept is found in *At the Mountains of Madness:* "Lake whimsically recall[ed] the primal myths about Great Old Ones who filtered down from the stars and concocted earth-life as a joke or mistake" (*CF* 3.45).

14 idiot Chaos] The reference is to Azathoth (XXII), not Nyarlathotep (who is the "Crawling Chaos"). Cf. "The Dreams in the Witch House": "the mindless entity Azathoth, which rules all time and space from a curiously environed black throne at the centre of Chaos" (*CF* 3.255).

blew Earth's dust away] Cf. Lovecraft's "Beyond the Wall of Sleep": "We shall meet again. . . . Perhaps in unremembered dreams . . . when the solar system shall have been swept away" (*CF* 1.84); and "The Crawling Chaos": "And when the smoke cleared away, and I sought to look upon the earth, I beheld against the background of cold, humorous stars only the dying sun and the pale mournful planets searching for their sister" (*CF* 4.36). Cf. also "Doom" from Donald Wandrei's *Sonnets of the Midnight Hours:* "The heavens . . . contained no thought or dust of thing or race" (*Sanctity and Sin* 125.5–6).

Discarded lines:

In the soft evening, at the old wood's rim
I see the evening star

The lines below, unlike those of *Fungi from Yuggoth,* are in alexandrines. They are found on leaf 8 of the draft of *Fungi from Yuggoth* (see p. 92), which contains the draft of "Antarktos."

> Nyarlathotep came out of Egypt with golden pshent,
> And called up the shadows from the polar continent,
> And all the dusty, brooding shapes from old forgotten graves,
> And serpents from the vaults of Shuggon beneath the waves.

Because they appear upside-down on the bottom of the sheet, they may have been intended for something other than *Fungi from Yuggoth.* The quatrain first appeared in *The Shuttered Room* 283.

XXII. Azathoth

Title: Cf. *CB* 49: "AZATHOTH—hideous name."; and *CB* 61: "A terrible pilgrimage to seek the nighted throne of the far daemon-sultan *Azathoth.*" The entries date to 1920. Also see n. 18 in Appendix A. The word *Azathoth,* if not the actual entity, apparently was of dream origin (see *OFF* 404). Lovecraft had planned in 1922 to write a novel titled *Azathoth* but produced only a small fragment. Azathoth is mentioned in several of Lovecraft's stories, most notably in *The Dream-Quest of Unknown Kadath,* where it is described as "that shocking final peril which gibbers unmentionably outside the ordered universe, where no dreams reach; that last amorphous blight of nethermost confusion which blasphemes and bubbles at the centre of all infinity—the boundless daemon-sultan Azathoth, whose name no lips dare speak aloud, and who gnaws hungrily in inconceivable, unlighted chambers beyond time" (*CF* 2.100). But the appearance of the poem constituted the first time the word *Azathoth* appeared in print, some months before it again appeared briefly in "The Whisperer in Darkness."

    Azathoth, surely a word of Lovecraft's coinage, is similar to various terms of which he may have known. In demonology, Ashtaroth is a Crowned Prince of Hell, a male figure named after the Canaanite goddess Ashtoreth. Anathoth in Jordan is one of the cities given to "the children of Aaron" (Josh. 21:13, 18; 1 Chr. 6:54, 60), in the tribe of Benjamin. In alchemy, Azoth is the essential agent of transformation; the name given by ancient alchemists to Mercury, the animating spirit within all matter that makes transmutation possible.

2 Cf. IV.12: "past the starry voids"; and XXXIII.7: "brooding gulfs beyond the Zodiac's course." Note the contrast to "undimensioned worlds" in III.7.

3 Cf. "The White Ship": "In the land of Sona-Nyl there is neither time nor space" (CF 1.108); and "Hypnos": "time and space . . . at bottom possess no distinct and definite existence" (CF 1.327). This notion derives from Einstein and is echoed in Frank Belknap Long's story "The Hounds of Tindalos," WT (March 1929); cf. XXXII.7. See "The Dreams in the Witch House": "Time could not exist in certain belts of space, and by entering and remaining in such a belt one might preserve one's life and age indefinitely; never suffering organic metabolism or deterioration except for slight amounts incurred during visits to one's own or similar planes. One might, for example, pass into a timeless dimension and emerge at some remote period of the earth's history as young as before (CF 3.260).

4 Cf. "The Whisperer in Darkness": "the chaos that transcends form and force and symmetry. . . . the monstrous nuclear chaos beyond angled space . . . cloaked under the name of Azathoth" (CF 2.520–21). Similar descriptions are found in other stories.

4–5 Cf. "The Haunter of the Dark": "He thought of the ancient legends of Ultimate Chaos, at whose centre sprawls the blind idiot god Azathoth, Lord of All Things, encircled by his flopping horde of mindless and amorphous dancers, and lulled by the thin monotonous piping of a daemoniac flute held in nameless paws" (CF 3.471).

10 flute] Cf. "The Festival": "the thin, whining mockery of a feeble flute" (CF 1.413). The flute sound occurs in other stories, particularly The Dream-Quest of Unknown Kadath. Lovecraft used similar images to indicate discordant sound, such as the cracked organ in "The Horror at Red Hook" (n. 34 in Appendix A) and "St. Toad's cracked chimes" (XXV).

13 Cf. V.1.

messenger] In *The Dream-Quest of Unknown Kadath*, Nyarlathotep is the "soul and messenger" of the "Other Gods" (*CF* 2.101). Apparently Nyarlathotep (cf. XXI) is the messenger, and also the daemon referred to in V. Note that Lovecraft had written a poem about another "messenger" (*not* Nyarlathotep) about a month previous to writing this sonnet.

Discarded lines:

Out into mindless lightless space he bore me
That black dreamed daemon Nyarlathotep

XXIII. Mirage

"Mirage" appeared in *WT* for February–March 1931 when Lovecraft was writing *At the Mountains of Madness:* "Our early flights . . . afforded some magnificent examples of the richly fantastic and deceptive mirages of the polar regions . . . Distant mountains floated in the sky as enchanted cities, and often the whole white world would dissolve into a . . . land of Dunsanian dreams and adventurous expectancy" (*CF* 3.23). Cf. *CB* 218 (c. April–May 1935): "Mirage in *time*—image of long-vanish'd pre-human city." Cf. n. 3 in Appendix A.

2 Cf. XIII.11 and "Despair":

> But the stream of Time, swift flowing,
> Brings the torment of half-knowing—
> Dimly rushing, blindly going
>   Past the never-trodden lea; (*AT* 61–62.17–20)

4–8 Cf. Lovecraft to Frank Belknap Long, 27 February 1931:

> I live in such worlds of endurable memory & dream & cosmic expansion & escape as my feeble creative powers are able to devise for me—always staving off the suicide-line by illusions of some future ability to get down on paper that quintessence of adventurous expectancy which the sight of a sunset beyond strange towers, or a little farmhouse against a rocky hill, or a rocky monolith in Leng as drawn by Nicholas Roerich, invariably excites within me. I don't believe, intellectually, that I can ever do it—but it is consoling to imagine that I might, through some accident. (*SL* 3.321)

5 lapping rivers] Cf. V.10.

Notes

6 labyrinths] Lovecraft describes the stone city in Antarctica in *At the Mountains of Madness* as a labyrinth. Cf. V.5.

7 skies of flame] Cf. XIII.1; and "Out of the Aeons": "the Day of the Sky-Flames" (*CF* 4.464).

13–14 These lines suggest Dyer's vision of the prehistoric Antarctic city before he actually explores it in *At the Mountains of Madness*.

XXIV. The Canal

Cf. *CB* 15: "Bridge & slimy black waters"; and *DS* 447 (3 October 1933): "Primal Basalt Bridge over the black and oily River Gnar" (given as Lovecraft's "address"). Lovecraft acknowledged use of the entry by his late note "Fungi—The Canal," but the entry itself does not seem as strong an influence as the story "The Canal" by Everil Worrell (*WT,* December 1927). Lovecraft wrote favorably of the story in "The Eyrie" of the June 1930 *WT.* His letter surely was written several months before actual publication, and so dates roughly to the time of the composition of *Fungi from Yuggoth* (as does a letter to August Derleth of 18 February 1930, also mentioning the story).

1–4 Cf. "The Music of Erich Zann": "The Rue d'Auseil lay across a dark river bordered by precipitous brick blear-windowed warehouses and spanned by a ponderous bridge of dark stone. . . . The river was also odorous with evil stenches which I have never smelled elsewhere" (*CF* 1.281).

5 Cf. "The Music of Erich Zann": "The houses were tall, peaked-roofed, incredibly old, and crazily leaning backward, forward, and sidewise. Occasionally an opposite pair, both leaning forward, almost met across the street like an arch" (*CF* 1.281); and "The Festival": "The upper part [of the house] overhung the narrow grass-grown street and nearly met the overhanging part of the house opposite, so that I was almost in a tunnel" (*CF* 1.408).

6 As the Rue d'Auseil in "The Music of Erich Zann."

9–12 Cf. "The Festival": "As the steps and the passage grew broader, I heard another sound, the thin, whining mockery of a feeble flute; and suddenly there spread out before me the boundless vista of an inner world—a vast fungous shore litten by a belching column of sick greenish flame and washed by a wide oily river that flowed from abysses frightful and unsus-pected to join the blackeſt gulfs of immemorial ocean" (*CF* 1.413).

10 oily water] See n. 19 in Appendix A. Cf. "The Rats in the Walls": "an oily river that flows under endless onyx bridges to a black, putrid sea" (*CF* 1.395); and "The Feſtival": "oily underground river" (*CF* 1.415).

11–12 Cf. "The Cats": "Black monſtrous bridges across oily rivers" (*AT* 72.5). In "The Whisperer in Darkness," there are "black rivers of pitch that flow under . . . myſterious Cyclopean bridges" (*CF* 2.518). See also Lovecraft to Donald Wandrei, 12 April 1927: "Odours at certain hours around the Great Bridge [in Providence] are not at all inviting, & the water has an oily, iridescent caſt which has more than once moved me to weird reflections" (*DW* 85).

12 Cf. "The Cats": "Flumes of futility swirling below (*AT* 72.2); and "He": "flume-like ſtreets" (*CF* 1.507).

Discarded lines:

<There is a meadow at an old wood's rim>
It is at twilight that the longing grows,
In quiet meadows near the old wood's rim,
When in the sunset's churning sea there swim
The young _____ & the

XXV. St. Toad's

Title: See n. 5 in Appendix A and also a letter to Clark Ashton Smith, (16 April 1927), for what appears to be the firſt mention of "St. Toad's":

> Meanwhile I have been enlarging my scenic background by a very minute ſtudy of *London* from books, maps, & pictures. [. . .] My researches have already given me one magnificently menacing *dream*—which left me this morning with a truly poignant sense of oppression & cosmic evil. I was searching through black & archaic alleys in Southwark, across London Bridge, for the rumoured & primordial Church of *St. Toad*, whereof men speak only in whispers, (as something always heard of at second or third hand) & in whose pre-Norman crypt a certain *influence* is reputed to lin-ger. I did not find it. (*DS* 129)

And another letter to Clark Ashton Smith, 12 May 1927 (*DS* 131): "In my vision I had crossed London Bridge to that selfsame tangle of archaic slums—seeking the horrible & fabulous church of St. Toad's, whose cracked chimes are heard of a morning by the mad & the moonstruck, above the wholesome music of healthier chimes." Thus, Lovecraft originally conceived of St. Toad's as being in London. The name is among the cancelled lines for "XIX. The Bells" (see notes there) and also in the listing ideas for poems on the manuscript page (Appendix A, n. 5).

During the Middle Ages, superstitions surrounding the toad in Europe linked it with the Christian devil, whose coat of arms was depicted with three toads. Witches were thought to use toads in their worship of the devil. Thus, the notion of a "St. Toad" is intended to be blasphemous, much as the Esoteric Order of Dagon of "The Shadow over Innsmouth." Lovecraft wrote of toadlike creatures in *The Dream-Quest of Unknown Kadath*, the source of many of the ideas and scenes in *Fungi from Yuggoth*. The St. Toad of 1929 (not 1927 as noted above) may have been suggested by Smith's Tsathoggua. Lovecraft first became acquainted with Tsathoggua when he read "The Tale of Satampra Zeiros" (*WT*, November 1931) in manuscript: "I must not delay in expressing my well-nigh delirious delight at 'The Tale of Satampra Zeiros'—which has veritably given me the one arch-kick of 1929!" (3 December 1929, *DS* 187). In the story, Smith describes Tsathoggua as "very squat and pot-bellied . . . like a monstrous toad." Lovecraft referred to Tsathoggua for the first time in "The Mound," written at about the time he was composing *Fungi from Yuggoth*, and made later references to it in other stories as well. Robert M. Price has maintained that the church in the poem seems to be based on St. Michael's Episcopal Church (first used in "The Festival") in Marblehead, Mass. (see Figure 12 in Shreffler, *The H. P. Lovecraft Companion* 69). The church in Marblehead is located on Frog Lane, which may have suggested Toad St[reet] to Lovecraft, and thus, when inverted, St. Toad. Cf. *DS* 437 (11 September 1933): "Abandoned Church of St. Toad in the Crumbling Slums of ancient Yothby" (given as Lovecraft's "address"). St. Toad's anticipates the "squat-towered stone church . . . built in a clumsy Gothic fashion" used by the Esoteric Order of Dagon in "The Shadow over

Innsmouth" (*CF* 3.175). The events of "St. Toad's" surely influenced "The Shadow over Innsmouth."

Lovecraft wrote of other debased churches or religious sects in "The Shadow over Innsmouth" and "The Haunter of the Dark."

Eden Phillpotts published a novel titled *The Chronicles of St. Tid* (1918), the first chapter of which is "The Church Grim."

1 cracked chimes] When the citizens of Marblehead heard of the signing of the Declaration of Independence, they rang the bell of St. Michael's church until it cracked. (The iconic Liberty Bell in Philadelphia acquired its own distinctive large crack sometime in the early 19th century.) Cf. "The Shadow over Innsmouth": "the raucous tones of a cracked bell" (*CF* 3.175). Recall the cracked organ in "The Horror at Red Hook," derived from *CB* 84: "Hideous cracked discords of bass musick from (ruin'd) organ in (abandon'd) abbey or cathedral"; and also n. 34 in Appendix A. The thrice-repeated warning "Beware St. Toad's cracked chimes!" echoes the thrice-repeated phrase "As I remember," in Donald Wandrei's "As I Remember" (later titled "The Torturers").

3–4 Cf. "The Shadow over Innsmouth": "One side of the cobblestoned open space was the straight line of the river; the other was a semicircle of slant-roofed brick buildings of about the 1800 period, from which several streets radiated away to the southeast, south, and southwest" (*CF* 3.176).

4 Cf. XXXVI.12.

8 Cf. The "jagged peaks of Thok" in XX. Also "The Shadow over Innsmouth": "Collapsing huddles of gambrel roofs formed a jagged and fantastic skyline, above which rose the ghoulish, decapitated steeple of an ancient church" (*CF* 3.181). This line is echoed in XXXIII.1.

9 The narrator of the poem is a tourist. Lovecraft often read guidebooks to places he visited and indeed wrote several guides or travelogues to cities of his travels, such as Charleston and Quebec. He was eager to see sights not mentioned in guidebooks, as is the narrator of "He." This line suggests Robert Olmstead's antiquarian jaunts in "The Shadow over Innsmouth": "Any reference to a town not shewn on common maps or listed in recent

guide-books would have interested me, and the agent's odd manner of allusion roused something like real curiosity. A town able to inspire such dislike in its neighbours, I thought, must be at least rather unusual, and worthy of a tourist's attention" (*CF* 3.161). Olmstead ignores the warnings of the travel agent. Also, cf. "Pickman's Model": "scores of the beasts crowded about one who held a well-known Boston guide-book and was evidently reading aloud. All were pointing to a certain passage, and every face seemed . . . distorted with epileptic and reverberant laughter" (*CF* 2.66).

12 croaked] Cf. the froglike manner of speech of the amphibian denizens of Innsmouth in "The Shadow over Innsmouth." The "greybeards" mentioned in the poem anticipate Zadok Allen of that story.

14 Cf. "The Haunter of the Dark": "Then suddenly a black spire stood out against the cloudy sky on his left, above the tier of brown roofs lining the tangled southerly alleys" (*CF* 3.456); cf. I.2. St. Michael's in Marblehead had no steeple for 221 years, until a new one was erected in 2014 for the church's three-hundredth anniversary.

Discarded lines [Note: These appear on the leaf that contains "The Canal," though they were numbered as though for sonnet XXV]:

I walked bewildered through the ancient streets
They warned me when I went into those lanes
South of the river where old houses sway.
Of the vague doom that wrinkled gossips say
Lurks

XXVI. The Familiars

Title: A familiar is a spirit, often in animal form, believed to act as a servant, as to a witch. In "The Dreams in the Witch House," Brown Jenkin (cf. note on XII) is Keziah Mason's familiar.

1 Whateley] In "The Dunwich Horror," several families in Dunwich bear the Whateley surname. Lovecraft there speaks of "undecayed Whateleys," implying there is also a degenerate branch of the family. Wizard Whateley and his grandson Wilbur also pored over what might be called "queer books."

5 Cf. Lovecraft's letter to his "intelligent ruſtick friend" Woodburn Harris of Vergennes, Vermont, of 9 November 1926: "are you so sensitive to the opinion of clods and machine-age barbarians that you would be worried by the myopic jackasses who might bray the old peasant ſtandby—'he made a good ſtart and was a good worker, but got to reading & began to let things slide until now he doesn't amount to a damn'" (*SL* 3.76–77).

7 Cf. "The Nameless City": "I alone have seen it, and that is why no other face bears such hideous lines of fear as mine" (*CF* 1.232).

9 night-howls] Cf. *CB* 138: "Someone or something cries in fright at sight of the rising moon, as if it were something ſtrange." Lovecraft's "x" on this entry in his notebook connotes use, although he does not indicate for what.

11 Aylesbury] Cf. VII.11. In "The Thing on the Doorſtep," the delirious Edward Derby is held in a cell at the "town farm" in Chesuncook, Maine.

13–14 Cf. *CB* 137 (c. 1925): "Strange man seen in lonely place talking with great winged thing which flies away as others approach"; and nn. 14 and 27 in Appendix A (although only n. 14 was crossed out to denote the idea was used). The night-gaunts (XX) are winged creatures. These lines suggeſt the dealings of the winged extraterreſtrials with human beings in "The Whisperer in Darkness": "Once a specimen was seen flying—launching itself from the top of a bald, lonely hill at night and vanishing in the sky after its great flapping wings had been silhouetted an inſtant againſt the full moon" (*CF* 2.470).

XXVII. The Elder Pharos

See Lovecraft to Clark Ashton Smith, 29 November 1933: "It was twilight, & the ancient roofs & boughs & towers & belfries of the hill were silhouetted blackly againſt a ſtill-orange sky. The windows of the downtown office buildings, juſt beginning to light up, made the lower town look like a conſtellation—and the great red beacon atop the 26-ſtory Induſtrial Truſt Building (which dominates the town as the Pharos dominated Alexandria) was blazing portentously" (*DS* 487–88). The Induſtrial Truſt Tower at 111 Weſtminſter Street (now the Bank of America Building) is the talleſt building in the city of Providence and the 28th talleſt in New England. It was conſtrućted in 1927. Lovecraft referred to it as a "pharos" as early as

March 1929 (*SL* 2.313). He mentions the red Industrial Trust beacon in "The Haunter of the Dark" (*CF* 3.454).

Title: In *At the Mountains of Madness,* Danforth's rant includes "'the elder pharos'" (*CF* 3.157).

1 Leng] Lovecraft mentions the plateau of Leng in several stories, the earliest allusion perhaps in "Beyond the Wall of Sleep" ("a bleak plateau in prehistoric Asia" [*CF* 1.84]); the actual name was first used in "Celephaïs" ("the cold desert plateau of Leng" [*CF* 1.189]), but no hint is given as to its location. In "The Hound," there is a reference to "the corpse-eating cult of inaccessible Leng, in Central Asia" (*CF* 1.343). But Lovecraft also located Leng in a dreamland in *The Dream-Quest of Unknown Kadath* before transferring it to Antarctica in *At the Mountains of Madness* (see *CF* 3.51). See Lovecraft to Robert Bloch (late May 1933, *RB* 32): "'Leng' is a cold & horrible plateau inhabited by a nameless race of priests who dwell in windowless stone towers & traffick with Outside powers. Human beings who seek out Leng never return." The Tsaidam Basin, in the northeastern section of the Plateau of Tibet, occupying the northern and western parts of Tsinghai province, China, is the site of a place called Leng-hu, but likely of too recent origin for Lovecraft to have known of it.

1–4 Cf. *The Dream-Quest of Unknown Kadath:* "At length a lone pallid light was seen on the skyline ahead, thereafter rising steadily as they approached, and having beneath it a black mass that blotted out the stars. Carter saw that it must be some beacon on a mountain, for only a mountain could rise so vast as seen from so prodigious a height in the air" (*CF* 2.200).

3 Cf. *The Case of Charles Dexter Ward:* "The nearest neighbours to his farm . . . one night remarked a great shaft of light shooting into the sky from some aperture in the roof of that cryptical stone building with the high, excessively narrow windows" (*CF* 2.253). In "The Colour out of Space," the mysterious "shaft of phosphorescence" (*CF* 2.393) does not merely shine out of Nahum Gardner's well, it *pours* out.

6 pharos] Pharos is the name of an island off Alexandria, Egypt, on which stood a lighthouse known as one of the Seven Wonders of the World in ancient times, built by Ptolemy Philadelphus (cf. *SL* 2.313). By extension,

any lighthouse is a pharos. Cf. *The Dream-Quest of Unknown Kadath:* "One ſtarlight evening . . . the Pharos shone splendid over the harbour" (*CF* 2.157). However, the pharos in the poem does not appear to be near a body of water.

7 Elder One] Cf. XV.8. In "Out of the Aeons," Lovecraft refers to the inhabitants of Yuggoth as the "Elder Ones."

8 Chaos] Cf. XXI.14.

9–12 Cf. *CB* 69: "Man with unnatural face—oddity of speaking—found to be a *mask*—Revelation." Also see nn. 16 and 23 in Appendix A (although only n. 16 was crossed out to designate the idea as used); and "Celephaïs": "the high-prieſt not to be described . . . wears a yellow silken mask over its face and dwells all alone in a prehiſtoric ſtone monaſtery on the cold desert plateau of Leng" (*CF* 1.189). The Thing is identical to "the high-prieſt not to be described, which wears a yellow silken mask over its face and prays to the Other Gods and their crawling chaos Nyarlathotep" in *The Dream-Quest of Unknown Kadath* (*CF* 2.172).

13 man's firſt youth] Lovecraft believed, as many did in his day, that "the human race ſtarted on some plateau in central Asia" (*MF* 207). Africa has since been considered the place of origin.

XXVIII. Expectancy

Title: Lovecraft used the word *expeɛtancy* to describe "the central keynote" of his personality. His descriptions of his famous initial visits to Marblehead and New York City perhaps beſt refleɛt what he meant by expectancy. In discussing the goal of weird literature with Harold S. Farnese, Lovecraft said that "the *sense of the unknown* is an authentic & virtually permanent—even though seldom dominant—part of the human personality" (22 September 1932, *ML* 258). The emotion is found throughout his fiction, though not always called "expeɛtancy." The earlieſt reference to expeɛtancy is found in "The Tree" (1920; *CF* 1.147), and it should be noted that Lovecraft does not refer to it only in his dreamland ſtories. In "The Silver Key," we encounter "viſtas of breathless expeɛtancy and unquenchable delight" (*CF* 2.74), but in "The Colour out of Space" we find "dread expectancy" (*CF* 2.386). To J. Vernon Shea, Lovecraft remarked (28 August 1931): "What we really enjoy is always the adventurous expectancy—seldom the realisation" (*JVS* 43).

2 Cf. *At the Mountains of Madness:* "the lure of the unplumbed is stronger in certain persons than most suspect" (*CF* 3.136).

3 Cf. XVIII, where there is no way to penetrate the gate; and also "Ex Oblivione": "Last night I swallowed the drug and floated dreamily into the golden valley and the shadowy groves; and when I came this time to the antique wall, I saw that the small gate of bronze was ajar" (*CF* 1.219).

6 pomps] I.e., pageants.

7 This line anticipates the method of traveling through space without the body in "The Whisperer in Darkness."

8 Cf. n. 35 in Appendix A.

9–12 These lines consolidate various key images found through *Fungi from Yuggoth:* "sunsets" (V.9, VIII.3, XII.11, XIII.1, XIV.1, XXIII.7, XXX.5, XXXV.3, XXXVI.9–10); "strange city spires" (III.10, VIII.11, XIII.1, XIX.8, XXI.10, XXV.14, XXXIII.1); "old villages" (I, VII.1, IX, XIX.7–8, XXIII.10, XXX.2, XXXIII); "woods" (IV.2, VII.3, XXXIV.1); "south winds" (XIV); "the sea" (I.3, V.6, VIII, XIX, XXXIII, XXXV); "low hills" (XXVI.2, XXXI); "lighted towns" (XXX.2); "old gardens" (XVIII); "keys" III, XXXVI.8; "gateways" (V.9, IX.7, XIII.10, XIX.11, XXXI.10); and "half-heard songs," primarily half-heard melodies (XIX.1–2, XXIII.12, XXIX.14). In his letter to Harold S. Farnese of 22 September 1932, Lovecraft discussed these themes as typifying his sense of expectancy:

> In my own efforts to crystallize spaceward outreaching, I try to utilize as many as possible of the elements which have, under earlier mental and emotional conditions, given man a symbolic feeling of the unreal, the ethereal, & the mystical—choosing those least attacked by the realistic mental and emotional conditions of the present. Darkness—sunset—dreams—mists—fever—madness—the tomb—the hills—the sea—the sky—the wind—all these, & many other things have seemed to me to retain a certain imaginative potency despite our actual scientific analyses of them. Accordingly I have tried to weave them into a kind of shadowy

phantasmagoria which may have the same sort of vague coherence as a cycle of traditional myth or legend—with nebulous backgrounds of Elder Forces & trans-galactic entities which lurk about this infinitesimal planet, (& others of course as well), establishing outposts thereon, & occasionally brushing aside other accidental forms of life (like human beings) in order to take up full habitation. (*SL* 4.70)

9 Cf. *The Case of Charles Dexter Ward:* "one of [Ward's] first memories is of the great westward sea of hazy roofs and domes and steeples and far hills which he saw one winter afternoon from that great railed embankment, all violet and mystic against a fevered, apocalyptic sunset of reds and golds and purples and curious greens" (*CF* 2.222).

10 downs] Open expanses of elevated land.

Discarded lines:

It is in sunsets & strange city <towers> spires
Old villages & gardens & misty downs,
<The sea, the lights of evening, 7 the flowers>
Of distant gardens, the hill, & lighted towns
At evening, & the sky's nocturnal fires
But though <without it __ our lives> its gleam alone makes life worth living,
None finds its goals or <guesses> learns what it <means> would mean.
None gains or guesses what it has to give.
None gains or learns the prize it <has to give> hints at giving."
None gains the promised goal or learns the meaning

But though without it we
Without that lure one would not care to live,
Yet none has wondered or guessed what it

XXIX. Nostalgia

The theme of "Nostalgia" is similar to that of Poe's "The City in the Sea." Lovecraft mentions Poe's "shocking spires and domes under the sea" in "Supernatural Horror in Literature" (*CE* 2.101). "The East India Brick Row," written about a month before *Fungi from Yuggoth*, contains an image similar to that found in the sestet of "Nostalgia":

So if at last a callous age must tear
    These jewels from the old town's quiet dress,
I think the harbour streets will always wear
    A puzzled look of wistful emptiness.

And strangers, staring spaciously along
    An ordered green that ponderous pylons frame,
Will always stop to wonder what is wrong,
    And miss some vital thing they cannot name. (*AT* 309.41–48)

Cf. n. 3 in Appendix A.

Title: Nostalgia is "a form of melancholia caused by prolonged absence from one's home or country; severe home-sickness" (*OED*). It is the precise word to describe Lovecraft's feeling for Providence during his "New York exile" of 1924–26. In "The Silver Key," Randolph Carter was "homesick for ethereal lands he no longer knew how to find" (*CF* 2.77).

4–8 These lines recall XVIII and have a similar Oriental tone.

9–12 Cf. "The Doom That Came to Sarnath": "These men indeed went to the lake to view Sarnath; but though they found the vast still lake itself, and the grey rock Akurion which rears high above it near the shore, they beheld not the wonder of the world and pride of all mankind. Where once had risen walls of three hundred cubits and towers yet higher, now stretched only the marshy shore, and where once had dwelt fifty millions of men now crawled only the detestable green water-lizard" (*CF* 1.130–31).

12 Cf. "The Nightmare Lake": "There shone, unnumbered fathoms down, / The tow'rs of a forgotten town" (*AT* 70.37–38).

13–14 See Lovecraft to Lillian D. Clark, 26 December 1925:

I found all present except Loveman, who is detained at work these evenings because of the opening of his employers' new shop; & was equally pleased & surprised to see good old *Mortonius,* whom I had thought on his way home to Sudbury. It seems that he had deferred his departure till Thursday, in order that he might be with us on this occasion—& he signalised his presence most nobly by acting as Santa Claus to the entire group—giving each member some appropriate gift from the ten-cent ſtore, with accompanying verses by himself. Mine was a bizarre paper-weight of exactly the sort to appeal to a Dunsanian fantaisiſte—a globe of glass about three inches in diameter, set in a black base & containing within it a *caſtle* with white walls & red roof, whose open door & windows yawn weirdly & alluringly. The entire globe is filled with water—or some analogous fluid—& when shaken becomes permeated with white flakes, as if a snowſtorm were raging about the lone tower. I, however, prefer to regard the tower as a ſtrange edifice of forgotten Atlantis, long sunken under the sea, & inhabited by siniſter & terrible polypous *things*, which float ghoulishly about in the cryptic currents of the deep. (*LFF* 525–26)

Tennyson's "The Kraken" (1830) mentions "unnumbered and enormous polypi" (l. 9). Lovecraft owned *The Works of Alfred Lord Tennyson, Poet Laureate* (New York: Grosset & Dunlap, [1892]–[1911]; *LL* 949).

Discarded lines:

They ſtrain to reach that fragrant, far-off shore,
Where marble walls & pyramids loom high
Againſt the deep blue of a blazing sky
Always they watch for the tall beacon-tower
That marks the harbour of the land they seek
They seek the marble tower that marks the shore
The marble beacon & the city's towers—
The rising city
But only empty waters ſtretch

XXX. Background

Title: "Background" is "That which lies at the back of or behind the chief objects of contemplation" (*OED*). Lovecraft considered New England, especially Providence, and his heritage to be the "background" of his life. See his letter to James F. Morton of 19 November 1929:

> The paſt is *real*—it is *all there is*. The present is only a trivial & momentary boundary-line—whilſt the future, though wholly determinate, is too essentially unknown and landmarkless to possess any hold upon our sense of concrete aeſthetic imagery. It is, too, liable to involve shifts & contraſts repugnant to our emotions & fancy; since we cannot ſtudy it as a unified whole & become accuſtomed to its internal variations as we can

study & grow accuśtomed to the vary'd paśt. There is nothing in the future to tie one's loyalties & affeċtions to—it can mean nothing to us, because it involves none of those mnemonic association-links upon which the illusion of meaning is based. (*JFM* 180)

See also Lovecraft to Bernard Auśtin Dwyer, June 1927: "All genuine art, I think, is local and rooted in the soil; for even when one sings of far incredible twilight lands he is merely singing of his homeland in some gorgeous and exotic mantle" (*MWM* 447); and Lovecraft to Clark Ashton Smith, 7 November 1930:

I want to know what śtretches *Outside*, & to be able to *visit* all the gulfs & dimensions beyond Space and Time. I want, too, to juggle the calendar at will; bringing things from the immemorial paśt down into the present, & making long journeys into the forgotten years. But I want the familiar Old Providence of my childhood as a perpetual base for these excursions—& in a good part of these necromancies & excursions I want certain transmuted features of Old Providence to form parts of the alien voids I visit or conjure up. (*DS* 263)

So śtrong was the notion of "background" to Lovecraft that he had no qualms about inviting his aunt Lillian to join him and his new bride at their home in New York City in order for her to give their household the necessary "sense of background" (18 March 1924, *LFF* 113). It is unlikely that Sonia Lovecraft would have shared in relishing such "background."

5–8 Cf. *The Case of Charles Dexter Ward:* "[Ward] liked mośtly to reach [the place] in the late afternoon, when the slanting sunlight touches the Market House and the ancient hill roofs and belfries with gold, and throws magic around the dreaming wharves where Providence Indiamen used to ride at anchor. After a long look he would grow almośt dizzy with a poet's love for the sight, and then he would scale the slope homeward in the dusk paśt the old white church and up the narrow precipitous ways where yellow gleams would begin to peep out in small-paned windows and through fanlights set high over double flights of śteps with curious wrought-iron railings" (*CF* 2.224).

7 Georgian śteeples] Striċtly speaking, "Georgian" in this sense refers to the age of King George I–IV in England (1714–1830). Here Lovecraft refers

to a corresponding Georgian age in architecture in New England, and specifically to the First Baptist (1775) and First Unitarian (1816) churches in Providence.

9 leaven] "An agency which produces profound change by progressive inward operation. Chiefly with allusion to certain passages of the gospels (e.g., Matt. 13.33; 16.60)" (*OED*).

9–12 These lines recall Randolph Carter's sampling and rejection of various "modern freedoms" in "The Silver Key."

XXXI. The Dweller

The scene described herein closely parallels the story lines of "The Statement of Randolph Carter" and "The Shadow out of Time." Beings who live underground are found in "The Statement of Randolph Carter," "The Nameless City," "The Call of Cthulhu," "Pickman's Model," *At the Mountains of Madness*, and "The Shadow out of Time." Cf. *CB* 165: "Terrible trip to an ancient & forgotten tomb." However, the events in the poem do not necessarily take place in a cemetery, and in any case the entry may actually have been made after the poem was written.

Title: Cf. n. 27 in Appendix A.

1 This line recalls the relative ages of the cities of Sarnath and older Ib in "The Doom That Came to Sarnath." Cf. "Nemesis": "I was old when the Pharaohs first mounted / The jewel-deck'd throne by the Nile" (*AT* 47.41–42); and "The Festival": "older than Bethlehem and Babylon, older than Memphis and mankind" (*CF* 1.406). In *At the Mountains of Madness* and "The Shadow out of Time," Lovecraft describes incredibly ancient races in a way that makes creatures of the earth's remote past seem relatively recent. Babylon was the capital of southern Mesopotamia (Babylonia) from the early second millennium to the early first millennium BCE and capital of the Neo-Babylonian (Chaldean) Empire in the seventh and sixth centuries BCE. Cf. "The Nameless City": "the nameless city, crumbling and inarticulate . . . must have been thus . . . while the bricks of Babylon were yet unbaked" (*CF* 1.231).

3 Cf. "The Nameless City": "sand-choked were all of the dark apertures near me, but I cleared one with my spade and crawled through it" (*CF* 1.234).

6–7 Cf. "The Nameless City": "Rich, vivid, and daringly fantastic designs and pictures formed a continuous scheme of mural painting . . . The importance of these crawling creatures [depicted] must have been vast, for they held first place among the wild designs on the frescoed wall and ceiling" (*CF* 1.239–40). The lines anticipate the cities of ancient civilizations in *At the Mountains of Madness* and "The Shadow out of Time."

9 Cf. "lava stairs" in XXXIV.11. There are many instances of the psychologically potent scene of downward-leading steps in Lovecraft's stories, including "The Tomb," "The Statement of Randolph Carter," "The Nameless City," "Facts concerning the Late Arthur Jermyn and His Family," "The Festival," "The Rats in the Walls," "The Call of Cthulhu," *The Dream-Quest of Unknown Kadath*, and "The Thing on the Doorstep." In *At the Mountains of Madness* and "The Shadow out of Time," legless but mobile entities gain access to the underground on inclined planes instead of steps.

9–10 Cf. "The Nameless City": "I . . . was aware of a great gate. . . . Reaching down from the passage into the abyss was the head of a steep flight of steps" (*CF* 1.242–43).

10 dolomite] The mineral calcium magnesium carbonate, a form of limestone.

12 elder signs] A general term, but note the "Elder Sign" in "The Messenger" (*AT* 80.7). Used variously in Lovecraft, most notably in *The Dream-Quest of Unknown Kadath*.

Discarded lines:

And then we found that gateway flanked with heads
Of nameless things that grinned in evil stair

XXXII. Alienation

Cf. *CB* 20: "Man journeys into the past—or imaginative realm—leaving bodily shell behind." This entry, and also *CB* 156 (see note under main title), describe the overall events of *Fungi from Yuggoth*. Lovecraft's later tales "The Whisperer in Darkness" and "The Shadow out of Time" have themes similar to that of this sonnet. Also see n. 35 in Appendix A.

1 Cf. "From Beyond": "'We shall overleap time, space, and dimensions, and without bodily motion peer to the bottom of creation'" (*CF* 1.194); and "I felt that I was about to dissolve or in some way lose the solid form" (*CF* 1.198). "The Thing on the Doorstep" contains reference to extracorporeal travel: "hideous exchanges of personality that permitted explorations in remote and forbidden places, on other worlds, and in different space-time continua" (*CF* 3.336).

1–2 Cf. "The Eidolon":

> When flesh upon its earthly bed
> Sprawls corpse-like and untenanted—
> Vacant of soul, which freely flies
> Thro' worlds unknown to waking eyes. (*AT* 57.5–8)

4–5 Cf. *The Dream-Quest of Unknown Kadath*: "Kuranes was the one soul who had been to the star-gulfs and returned free from madness" (*CF* 2.102); and "The Whisperer in Darkness": "To visit Yuggoth would drive any weak man mad—yet I am going there" (*CF* 2.518).

5 Yaddith] This constitutes Lovecraft's first mention of *Yaddith*, a planet beyond our solar system. He used it at length in "Through the Gates of the Silver Key" and mentions it in "The Diary of Alonzo Typer," and "The Haunter of the Dark." He also refers to a "Yaddith-Gho" throughout "Out of the Aeons." Lovecraft made numerous allusions to Yaddith in his letters, such as "9876 ⟶▪⟵th Pulse-Beat of the Cosmic Fungus enveloping Yaddith, in the Ætherless Gulf of Re-entrant Angles beyond the 8th Trans-Imaginational Ring of Finite Continua" (Lovecraft to Clark Ashton Smith, 25 December 1930, *DS* 283). The name is similar to that of Yadin the prophet in Dunsany's "Of the Thing That Is Neither God Nor Beast" (in *The Gods of Pegāna*). Lovecraft closes his letter to Smith of 15 October 1927, thanking him "for that nameless head from the black planet Yadoth" (*DS* 147).

6 Ghooric zone] Cf. "The Outpost": "the pest-mad zone" (*AT* 78.29). Lovecraft called New York "the pest zone"; perhaps this line recalls his New York experience and his "safe" return to Providence. This constitutes the only mention of *Ghooric* in Lovecraft's works, save for the closing of a letter to Robert Bloch dated 7 January 1937, where he refers to a "Ghooric Key" (*RB* 184). Lovecraft may have derived the word from Arthur Machen's *Voorish* sign in "The White People"; see "The Dunwich Horror" (*CF* 2.450). Lovecraft had described the plot of Machen's story in a letter to August Derleth in October 1929. See *OED, Ghurry:* "1. A space of time: a. In an old Hindoo custom, 24 minutes, the 60th part of a day of 24 hours; b. In Anglo-Indian usage, an hour. 2. A metal plate on which the hours are struck." In "Out of the Aeons," Lovecraft mentions a "Dhoric shrine." Dunsany coined the name *Rhoog* (of which *Ghoor-* is a partial anagram) in "The Sorrow of Search" in *Time and the Gods.*

7 curved space] The notion of curved space is from Einstein's theory of relativity and is found in Frank Belknap Long's "The Hounds of Tindalos" (*WT*, March 1929). Cf. "The Whisperer in Darkness": *"the last curved rim of space"* (*CF* 2.496); also XIV.7. See "The Dreams in the Witch House": "their progress had not been in a straight line, but rather along the alien curves and spirals of some ethereal vortex which obeyed laws unknown to the physics and mathematics of any conceivable cosmos" (*CF* 3.255)

8 Cf. XXII.9–10. See "The Dreams in the Witch House": "Eventually there had been a hint of . . . the thin, monotonous piping of an unseen flute" (*CF* 3.255); and *At the Mountains of Madness:* "the howling, piping wind that raced through the pass" (*CF* 3.70).

9 This line recalls Lovecraft's Eben Spencer dream, described in *Letters to Alfred Galpin* 71–73 and very briefly noted in *CB* 9, in which Dr. Chester ages prematurely because of his experiments; Crawford Tillinghast in "From Beyond," who appears to have aged from his experience in another dimension; and *The Case of Charles Dexter Ward*, in which Ward "seemed oddly older than his twenty-six years would warrant" after he was displaced by Joseph Curwen (*CF* 2.215). See also XXVI.7. See Lovecraft to Robert E. Howard, 4 October 1930:

To read of the experiences of the Rev. Cotton Mather, and of his preco-
cious little brother Nathaniel (who virtually tormented himself to death
with hysterical emotional 'soul-questioning') is to witness genuine tragedy—the tragedy of ignorance and superstition. Poor little Nat died at
19—I have seen his gravestone in the old Charter St. Burying Ground at
Salem. His fortunate escape from life came in 1688, and his epitaph (a
tribute to his prodigious learning) reads with unconscious pathos—"An
Aged Person who had seen but 19 Winters in the World." (*MF* 67)

9–12 Cf. "From Beyond": "Over and above the luminous and shadowy
chaos arose a picture which, though vague, held the elements of consistency
and permanence. . . . of all the space unoccupied by familiar material objects
not one particle was vacant" (*CF* 1.198–99); and "The Book":

> . . . when morning found me in the attic room I saw in the walls and
> shelves and fittings that which I had never seen before.
>
> Nor could I ever after see the world as I had known it. Mixed with
> the present scene was always a little of the past and a little of the future,
> and every once-familiar object loomed alien in the new perspective
> brought by my widened sight. (pp. 236–37)

13–14 These lines echo "Polaris," in which the unnamed dreamer cannot
get back to the real world; "The Outsider," in which the ghoul seeks fruit-
lessly to join the crowd of revellers; and "The Strange High House in the
Mist," in which "the man who came down from that crag was not wholly
the man who went up, and . . . somewhere under that grey peaked roof, or
amidst inconceivable reaches of that sinister white mist, there lingered still
the lost spirit of him who was Thomas Olney" (*CF* 2.95). In "Through the
Gates of the Silver Key," the transformed Randolph Carter struggles to fit
into society. The entire sestet of the poem anticipates Nathaniel Wingate
Peaslee's "amnesia" in "The Shadow out of Time."

XXXIII. Harbour Whistles

Title: Cf. "The Horror at Red Hook": "the monstrous organ litanies of the
harbour whistles" (*CF* 1.484); "He": "deep horns bayed weird harmonies"
(*CF* 1.506); and n. 22 in Appendix A. The stories cited take place in New
York City. Cf. Lovecraft's enthusiastic descriptions of the sounds of the
New York harbor from his visit in 1924: "Added to the weird lights are the

weird sounds of the port, where the traffick of all the world comes to a focus. Fog-horns, ships' bells, the creak of distant windlasses. [. . .] Ah, me! Would that I could express the magick of the scene!" (29–30 September 1924, *LFF* 172).

6 Cf. "The Thing on the Doorstep": "some damnable, utterly accursed focus of unknown and malign cosmic forces" (*CF* 3.341).

7 Zodiac's course] Cf. III.11.

8 The word *Om*, ॐ, of ancient India is considered to be the "cosmic sound," the "mystical syllable," the universal sound that vibrates in the universe. Typically it is uttered as a long, sustained chant for the equivalent of several breaths. Cf. "The Music of Erich Zann" for a somewhat different cosmic tone: "And then I thought I heard a shriller, steadier note that was not from the viol; a calm, deliberate, purposeful, mocking note from far away in the west" (*CF* 1.288).

9–12 Cf. "The Haunter of the Dark": "he was looking at the stone again, and letting its curious influence call up a nebulous pageantry in his mind. He saw processions of robed, hooded figures whose outlines were not human, and looked on endless leagues of desert lined with carved, sky-reaching monoliths. He saw towers and walls in nighted depths under the sea, and vortices of space where wisps of black mist floated before thin shimmerings of cold purple haze. And beyond all else he glimpsed an infinite gulf of sheer darkness" (*CF* 3.464–65).

11–14 Cf. "From Beyond" (in a somewhat different context): "Then, from the farthermost regions of remoteness, the *sound* softly glided into existence. It was infinitely faint, subtly vibrant, and unmistakably musical" (*CF* 1.197).

Discarded lines:

Cries from far ports & fabulous seas & white
Beaches of coral; _____ in haunting choirs
Far <beaches wail in> isles of coral chant in brooding choirs
Yet all half-blended by some brooding force
Focused from guess beyond the Zodiac's course,
And into one mysterious pattern thrown

XXXIV. Recapture

This sonnet was not initially part of *Fungi from Yuggoth* and antedates it by a little more than a month. It was inserted c. June 1936 at the suggestion of R. H. Barlow (see commentary); but see n. 26 in Appendix A. See Lovecraft to Clark Ashton Smith, 19 November 1929: "The other day I couldn't resist putting a recent dream-tableau into metrical form—although I'm well aware of my poetic limitations. If I don't get disgusted with it on re-peated re-perusal, I may try it on Wright—for if it lands it would bring in $3.00 as a filler. The dream itself was marvellously poignant—but I didn't succeed in catching much of the feeling in the lines" (*Dreams and Fancies* 28). *WT* accepted the poem and paid $3.50 for it (HPL to James F. Morton, 6 December 1929, *JFM* 205).

1 heath] Open uncultivated ground; an extensive tract of waste land, as the "blasted heath" of "The Colour out of Space."

5 The wind, a recurrent image throughout *Fungi from Yuggoth*, is notice-ably absent in this sonnet. Similar effects are found in "The Music of Erich Zann": "And I recall that there was no wind" (*CF* 1.290); and "The Colour out of Space": "there was no wind at that hour of the evening" (*CF* 2.392).

8 Lovecraft was ghostwriting "The Mound" at the time he wrote "Recap-ture" and *Fungi from Yuggoth*.

10 Cf. IV.5.

12 The Giant's Causeway in Ireland contains structures suggestive of stairs "to vast for human tread." Although the pyramids of Egypt can be climbed, the blocks are too large to be walked up as a staircase.

14 I.e., an existence as transient as a dream. Cf. "The Call of Cthulhu": "man and the world seem recent and transient indeed" (*CF* 2.38).

Discarded lines:

There was no wind & not a trace of sound
No sound or
There was no living thing & not a sound
Or any stunted shrub or twisted tree
Nor any view ahead—till suddenly

Notes

I ~~spy'd~~ saw a ~~mound~~ great mound looming in my way

I shrieked ~~for now~~ & knew what primal ſtar & year
Had clutched me back from the ~~sleight~~ frail world of men!

XXXV. Evening Star

Numbered XXXIV at the time of composition in January 1930. This sonnet
seems to be a retelling of "Polaris." Poe also wrote a poem titled "Evening
Star." Hesperus (see note on XIII) is the evening ſtar. Cf. "The Queſt of
Iranon": "I will attend thy songs at evening when the ſtars one by one bring
dreams to the minds of dreamers" (*CF* 1.251).

7 evening ſtar] The "evening ſtar" is the planet Venus, but Jupiter and Mer-
cury are also called evening ſtars when observed in the weſt after sunset. By
"evening ſtar" Lovecraft surely meant a planet, for no ſtar could be inhabited
as indicated by the "towers and gardens" in l. 11. In "The Poe-et's Nightmare," Lucullus Languish, "ſtudent of the skies" (l. 1) "scour'd the heav'ns
far / Searching for raptures in the evening ſtar" (ll. 15–16). Writing to
Woodburn Harris c. 1 March 1929, Lovecraft ſtates: "Resplendent Venus
and Jupiter shine close together, hanging over the great beacon-tower of
the terraced Induſtrial Truſt Building as they used to hang 2000 years ago
over the towering Pharos in Alexandria's crowded harbor" (*SL* 2.313).

14 Cf. "Beyond the Wall of Sleep": "I perceived a slight blurring and fading
of the objeĉts around us, as though some force were recalling me to earth"
(*CF* 1.81); and n. 28 in Appendix A.

XXXVI. Continuity

Numbered XXXV at the time of composition in January 1930.

Title: Continuity is perhaps the main theme of *Fungi from Yuggoth,* and
thus is fitly addressed in the concluding poem of the sequence. Cf. "The
Horror at Red Hook": "They chilled and fascinated him more than he
dared confess to his associates . . . for he seemed to see in them some monſtrous thread of secret continuity; some fiendish, cryptical, and ancient
pattern utterly beyond and below the sordid mass of faĉts and habits and
haunts" (*CF* 1.485); and "The Dunwich Horror": "the scattered senses of
poor Curtis Whateley began to knit back into a sort of continuity" (*CF*

2.465). But perhaps the best articulation of the concept is found in "The Haunter of the Dark": "[Blake] glimpsed an infinite gulf of sheer darkness, where solid and semi-solid forms were known only by their windy stirrings, and cloudy patterns of force seemed to superimpose order on chaos and hold forth a key to all the paradoxes and arcana of the worlds we know" (*CF* 3.465). Continuity, like expectancy, can evoke terror, but primarily it evokes wonder.

In correspondence with J. Vernon Shea, Lovecraft articulated *continuity* as a key aspect of his personality, but not in any sense that we might expect. That is, he does not approach the emotion evoked by continuity so much as a fantaisiste or writer of horror fiction, but as, to use the epithet so aptly bestowed on him by Jason C. Eckhardt, a "cosmic Yankee":

> only through the preservation of an unbroken continuity can any civilisation grow or remain great. Foreigners were never repulsed in N.E. as long as they came in decently assimilable quantities. Only when vast hordes of them virtually swamped us did sharp lines of cleavage arise. And even these lines are not *consciously* drawn. It is simply that people as utterly antipodal as New Englanders & the invading Latin-Slav type cannot possibly, in the normal course of events, have any thoughts or feelings or aspirations in common. There is absolutely nothing for us & them to say to each other . . . . a condition perfectly inevitable, & involving neither praise nor blame on either side. The only *fault* is our criminal folly in ever admitting these alien hordes. We did it through anthropological & sociological ignorance, plus a naive swallowing of the idealistic flapdoodle of political hypocrites. [*JVS* 195]

> [. . .] Everything really desirable in life is the result of *stability* & *continuity*—since, outside the narrow radius of crude animal sensation, virtually nothing has any interest or meaning apart from the associations twined around it through generations of racial experience. That is why the machine age tends so greatly to impoverish life—by removing us from our hereditary adjustment to the landscape, the seasons, the agricultural cycle, the acts of daily life & industry, & the familiar concepts of distance dependent upon transportational speed. (8–22 November 1933, *JVS* 204)

For Lovecraft, his surroundings created in him a linkage with his environment and also with the past. As an adult, he despised the modern era, the

Machine Age, and all it represented. His aesthetic sense was anchored in the eighteenth century, and also in the Roman era, and he clung to a mental image of those bygone times. Of course, eighteenth-century America was the more easily recognizable in the rural Rhode Island where Lovecraft grew up. He did not welcome the loss of those scenes to modernity, nor the influx of "foreigners" of various stripes into the pastoral ideal of his memory and imagination.

Lovecraft's racism, virulent though it could be, seems not so much to be misanthropic or xenophobic, but instead deeply rooted in his fervent desire to maintain a sense of continuity with the past, with his background (the concept evoked in sonnet XXX). Nearly all his friends and associates found him to be the kindest and most considerate of persons they had met or known. But he could not bear to see his personal sense of continuity with the New England of his youth being breached by the numerous changes brought by rapidly changing times.

3–4 Here Lovecraft does not speak of *ether* in the sense of an undetectable substance permeating all space and transmitting waves of light and energy, thought to exist by some scientists in Lovecraft's day, although the sense is the same. He merely tries to articulate how something, almost like an utterly intangible substance, seems to link the present to the ancient past.

6 outward eyes] I.e., eyes as sensory receptors, as opposed to inward eyes— one's own imagination.

7–8 Cf. "The Shadow over Innsmouth": "the golden light of late afternoon gave the ancient roofs and decrepit chimneys an air of mystic loveliness and peace" (*CF* 3.201)

8 hidden keys]. See note to III.

9–14 Cf. Lovecraft to Donald Wandrei, 21 April 1927:

The vistas I relish most are those in which the sunset plays a transfiguring & glorifying part. Sometimes I stumble accidentally on rare combinations of slope, curved street-line, roofs & gables & chimneys, & accessory details of verdure & background [cf. XXX], which in the magic of late afternoon assume a mystic majesty & exotic significance beyond the power of words to describe. Absolutely nothing else in life now has the power to move me so much; for in these momentary vistas there seem to open before me bewildering avenues to all the wonders & lovelinesses I have ever sought, & to all those gardens of eld [cf. XVIII] whose memory trembles just beyond the rim of conscious recollection, yet close enough to lend to life all the significance it possesses [cf. XXVIII.14]. All that I live for is to recapture some fragment of this hidden & unreachable beauty; this beauty which is all of dream, yet which I feel I have known closely & revelled in through long aeons before my birth or the birth of this or any world. There is somewhere, my fancy fabulises, a marvellous city of ancient streets & hills & gardens & marble terraces, wherein I once lived happy eternities, & to which I must return if ever I am to have content. Its name & place I know not . . . but every now & then there flashes some intimation of it in the travelled paths of men. Of this cryptic & glorious city—this primal & archaic place of splendour in Atlantis or Cockaigne or the [Garden of the] Hesperides [cf. XIII]—many towns of earth hold vague & elusive symbols that peep furtively out at certain moments, only to disappear again. (*DW* 98)

Also cf. "The Whisperer in Darkness": "The town . . . drowsed like the older New England cities which one remembers from boyhood, and something in the collocation of roofs and steeples and chimneys and brick walls formed contours touching deep viol-strings of ancestral emotion" (*CF* 2.509). Such sentiments and scenes abound in Lovecraft's writings, especially in *The Case of Charles Dexter Ward* written shortly before the letter quoted above: "He liked mostly to reach this point in the late afternoon, when the slanting sunlight touches the Market House and the ancient hill roofs and belfries with gold, and throws magic around the dreaming wharves where Providence Indiamen used to ride at anchor. After a long look he would grow almost dizzy with a poet's love for the sight, and then he would scale the slope homeward in the dusk past the old white church and up the narrow precipitous ways where yellow gleams would begin to peep out in small-paned windows and through fanlights set high over double flights of steps with curious wrought-iron railings" (*CF* 2.224). Cf. *CB* 93: "A place one has been—a beautiful view of a village or farm-dotted valley in the sunset—which one cannot find again or locate in memory"; and *CB* 94: "Change comes over the sun—shews objects in strange form, perhaps restoring landscape of the past."

Notes

Discarded lines:

Through all his life he saw them rising there—
Faint, grey, & misty in the unknown west;
Glimpsed from old streets that wandered up the west

In mouldy volumes, piled up in garret gloom;
Old houses have it, & brown <crumbling books> tattered tomes;
Grey hills, & flat lands in the evening light;
Forests <, green mossy walls,> & narrow roads that stretch from sight
Between low moss-grown walls &

Appendix A
Notes for Additional Sonnets

H. P. Lovecraft made numerous notes on the manuscript of "XIX. The Bells" (see page 95) as ideas for additional poems to include in *Fungi from Yuggoth*. They represent very brief impressions, less defined than even the entries in his commonplace book, and derive primarily from *The Dream-Quest of Unknown Kadath* and certain of his published works. Many of the notes inspired sonnets XX through XXXV (excluding "Recapture"). The items listed below, reading down the manuscript page, left to right in approximate snaking columns, are numbered to facilitate referencing in the Notes section. The strikeouts are Lovecraft's, presumably to indicate notes he employed in the composition of the final sixteen poems. Note that n. 1 and n. 4 are identical. Lovecraft must have noticed the duplication and then struck out the supernumerary item; it does not appear to have suggested any particular sonnet. The editor's conjectural association of notes to other poems is indicated by "?".

[1]	far music in sky	
[2]	valley bars where cosmic voices sound	
[3]	memory of lost land	[XXIX?]
[4]	~~far music in sky~~	[XIX?]
[5]	~~St. Toad's~~	[XXV]
[6]	~~night-gaunts~~	[XX]
[7]	messenger comes to lead away	
[8]	~~migrations of birds~~	[XXIX]
[9]	slipping through time	[XXIII?]
[10]	rutted road	
[11]	ghost of mood	
[12]	bird in ancient ruins speaks	
[13]	~~vague expectancy of adventure~~	[XXVIII]

[14]	~~man in lone place talking to great winged thing~~	[XXVI]
[15]	~~wistful impression—in country lane~~	[XXIII]
[16]	~~yellow wizard~~	[XXVII]
[17]	~~Nyarlathotep~~	[XXI]
[18]	~~Azathoth~~	[XXII]
[19]	~~black oily water under bridges~~	[XXIV]
[20]	~~light across distant valley~~	[XXXVI?]
[21]	quest for something undefined	[XXIII?]
[22]	~~harbour whistles in the night~~	[XXXIII]
[23]	"man" shewn to be *thing* wearing mask	[XXVII?]
[24]	distant mts. seen from seaport	
[25]	plains stretching W & S to great city	
[26]	musick? / Recapture of past	[XXXIV had been completed previously]
[27]	Evil dweller in hills	[XXVI?]
[28]	bondage to other planet	[XXXV?]
[29]	Sabbat—meet neighbours in strange wild place	
[30]	city suddenly deserted	[XXIX?]
[31]	Green Meadow	
[32]	Crawling Chaos	[XXI]
[33]	twilight city—slinking shapes not human	
[34]	cracked bass organ notes in a sumptuous st.	
[35]	freedom—lost in space	[XXVIII?]

Items that have been identified are discussed under the appropriate poems in the commentary. The following previous compositions by Lovecraft seem to impinge on the poem: 10: "The Rutted Road" (1916); 26: "Recapture" (mid-November 1929), later assumed into the overall sequence as sonnet XXXIV; 30: "The City" (1919); 31: "The Green Meadow" (1918 or 1919); 32: "The Crawling Chaos"; 34: "The Horror at Red Hook" (1925).

Appendix B
[The Book]

My memories are very confused. There is even much doubt as to where they begin; for at times I feel appalling vistas of years stretching behind me, while at other times it seems as if the present moment were an isolated point in a grey, formless infinity. I am not even certain how I am communicating this message. While I know I am speaking, I have a vague impression that some strange and perhaps terrible mediation will be needed to bear what I say to the points where I wish to be heard. My identity, too, is bewilderingly cloudy. I seem to have suffered a great shock—perhaps from some utterly monstrous outgrowth of my cycles of unique, incredible experience.

These cycles of experience, of course, all stem from that worm-riddled book. I remember when I found it—in a dimly lighted place near the black, oily river where the mists always swirl. That place was very old, and the ceiling-high shelves full of rotting volumes reached back endlessly through windowless inner rooms and alcoves. There were, besides, great formless heaps of books on the floor and in crude bins; and it was in one of these heaps that I found the thing. I never learned its title, for the early pages were missing; but it fell open toward the end and gave me a glimpse of something which sent my senses reeling.

There was a formula—a sort of list of things to say and do—which I recognised as something black and forbidden; something which I had read of before in furtive paragraphs of mixed abhorrence and fascination penned by those strange ancient delvers into the universe's guarded secrets whose decaying texts I loved to absorb. It was a key—a guide—to certain gateways and transitions of which mystics have dreamed and whispered since the race was young, and which lead to freedoms and discoveries beyond the three dimensions and realms of life and matter that we know. Not for centuries had any man recalled its vital substance or known where to find it, but this book was very old indeed. No printing-press, but the hand of some half-crazed monk, had traced these ominous Latin phrases in uncials of awesome antiquity.

I remember how the old man leered and tittered, and made a curious sign with his hand when I bore it away. He had refused to take pay for it, and only long afterward did I guess why. As I hurried home through those narrow, winding, mist-choked waterfront streets I had a frightful impression of being stealthily followed by softly padding feet. The centuried, tottering houses on both sides seemed alive with a fresh and morbid malignity—as if some hitherto closed channel of evil understanding had abruptly been opened. I felt that those walls and overhanging gables of mildewed brick and fungous plaster and timber—with fishy, eye-like, diamond-paned windows that leered—could hardly desist from advancing and crushing me . . . yet I had read only the least fragment of that blasphemous rune before closing the book and bringing it away.

I remember how I read the book at last—white-faced, and locked in the attic room that I had long devoted to strange searchings. The great house was very still, for I had not gone up till after midnight. I think I had a family then—though the details are very uncertain—and I know there were many servants. Just what the year was, I cannot say; for since then I have known many ages and dimensions, and have had all my notions of time dissolved and refashioned. It was by the light of candles that I read—I recall the relentless dripping of the wax—and there were chimes that came every now and then from distant belfries. I seemed to keep track of those chimes with a peculiar intentness, as if I feared to hear some very remote, intruding note among them.

Then came the first scratching and fumbling at the dormer window that looked out high above the other roofs of the city. It came as I droned aloud the ninth verse of that primal lay, and I knew amidst my shudders what it meant. For he who passes the gateways always wins a shadow, and never again can he be alone. I had evoked—and the book was indeed all I had suspected. That night I passed the gateway to a vortex of twisted time and vision, and when morning found me in the attic room I saw in the walls and shelves and fittings that which I had never seen before.

Nor could I ever after see the world as I had known it. Mixed with the present scene was always a little of the past and a little of the future, and every once-familiar object loomed alien in the new perspective brought by my widened sight. From then on I walked in a fantastic dream of unknown and half-known shapes; and with each new gateway crossed, the less plainly could I recognise the things of the narrow sphere to which I had so long been bound. What I saw about me none else saw; and I grew doubly silent and aloof lest I be thought mad. Dogs had a fear of me, for they felt the outside shadow which never left my side. But still I read more—in hidden, forgotten books and scrolls to which my new vision led me—and pushed through fresh gateways of space and being and life-patterns toward the core of the unknown cosmos.

I remember the night I made the five concentric circles of fire on the floor, and stood in the innermost one chanting that monstrous litany the messenger from Tartary had brought. The walls melted away, and I was swept by a black wind through gulfs of fathomless grey with the needle-like pinnacles of unknown mountains miles below me. After a while there was utter blackness, and then the light of myriad stars forming strange, alien constellations. Finally I saw a green-litten plain far below me, and discerned on it the twisted towers of a city built in no fashion I had ever known or read of or dreamed of. As I floated closer to that city I saw a great square building of stone in an open space, and felt a hideous fear clutching at me. I screamed and struggled, and after a blankness was again in my attic room, sprawled flat over the five phosphorescent circles on the floor. In that night's wandering there was no more of strangeness than in many a former night's wandering; but there was more of terror because I knew I was closer to those outside gulfs and worlds than I had ever been before. Thereafter I was more cautious with my incantations, for I had no wish to be cut off from my body and from the earth in unknown abysses whence I could never return.

Appendix C
Chronology of Appearances of *Fungi from Yuggoth*

1930

12 March	*Providence Journal*	*Nostalgia
26 March	*Providence Journal*	*Night-Gaunts
16 April	*Providence Journal*	*Background
May	*Weird Tales*	*Recapture [not yet part of the series]
	Silver Fern	*Harbour Whistles
7 May	*Providence Journal*	*The Dweller
14 May	*Providence Journal*	*The Well
July	*Driftwind*	*The Familiars
September	*Weird Tales*	*The Courtyard; *Star-Winds
September–October	*L'Alouette*	Harbour Whistles
October	*Weird Tales*	*Hesperia
November	*Driftwind*	*The Port
	Weird Tales	*Antarktos
December	*Weird Tales*	*The Bells

1931

January	*Weird Tales*	*Nyarlathotep; *Azathoth
February–March	*Weird Tales*	*Mirage; *The Elder Pharos
March	*Driftwind*	*The Lamp
April	*Driftwind*	*The Window
April–May	*Weird Tales*	*Alienation

*First appearance.

1932

March	*Driftwind*	*The Canal; *The Gardens of Yin
Spring	*Ripples from Lake Champlain*	*The Pigeon-Flyers; ["A Memory" was accepted but not published]
Summer	*Pioneer*	*Continuity
Autumn	*Pioneer*	*Evening Star
September	*Interesting Items*	Background
November	*Driftwind*	*The Howler

1933

May	*Harvest*	The Canal

1934

October	*Fantasy Fan*	*The Book; *Pursuit
	Driftwind	*Zaman's Hill
November	*Interesting Items*	Night-Gaunts

1935

January	*Fantasy Fan*	*The Key; *Homecoming
May–June	*Galleon*	Background ["Harbour Whistles" was accepted but not published]
November–December	*Phantagraph*	The Dweller

1936

February	*Causerie*	Continuity
June	*Phantagraph*	Night-Gaunts
July	*Phantagraph*	Nostalgia
20 August	*Lovecrafter*	Background
November	*Phantagraph*	Harbour Whistles
November–December	*Science-Fantasy Correspondent*	Homecoming
December	*Driftwind*	*Recognition

1937

April	*Driftwind*	The Book
May	*Science Fiction Bard*	Night-Gaunts
July	*Phantagraph*	The Well
8 July	[Cambridge, MD] *Democrat and News*	The Pigeon-Flyers; Homecoming; *A Memory; Night-Gaunts
Summer?	*HPL*	Homecoming; Nostalgia; Night-Gaunts; The Dweller; Harbour Whistles

1938		
January	*Weird Tales*	The Canal
1939		
February	*Weird Tales*	The Lamp; Zaman's Hill
May	*Weird Tales*	Harbour Whistles
June–July	*Weird Tales*	The Howler
August	*Weird Tales*	The Gardens of Yin
December	*Weird Tales*	Night-Gaunts
1940		
March	*Weird Tales*	The Dweller
1941		
May–June	*Phantagraph*	Continuity
1943		
June	*Fungi from Yuggoth* [FAPA]	[I–XXXIII only; *St. Toad's; *Expectancy]
Summer	*Acolyte*	Continuity
	Beyond the Wall of Sleep [Arkham House]	[first appearance of the entire sequence]
1944		
May	*Weird Tales*	St. Toad's [first magazine appearance]; Evening Star; Homecoming; The Well; The Window
1946		
January	*Weird Tales*	Recapture
September	*Weird Tales*	The Port
1947		
January	*Weird Tales*	The Familiars; The Pigeon-Flyers
March	*Weird Tales*	Continuity; A Memory
	Dark of the Moon	*Fungi from Yuggoth*
1963		
	Collected Poems	*Fungi from Yuggoth*
1982		
	Fungi from Yuggoth	[first textually sound edition]

Appendix D
Textual Variants

There are several important surviving manuscripts of *Fungi from Yuggoth*, and less significant copies of its individual poems. Documents 1 through 4, all held at the John Hay Library, are of primary interest.

---

1. "Recapture" (AMS, 1 p.), mid-November 1929. The manuscript is reproduced on page 105 of this edition. The sonnet, of course, antedates *Fungi from Yuggoth* and was incorporated into the long poem more than six years later. The draft, with its numerous strikeouts and interlineations, very much resembles the draft of the longer poem, except that Lovecraft here employed various archaic spellings (e.g., hump'd, suck'd).

---

2. *Fungi from Yuggoth* (AMS, 20 pp.), 27 December 1929–4 January 1930. The manuscript is reproduced on pp. 85–104 of this edition. The leaves are numbered (and the folios encircled). Initially, Lovecraft circled the Roman numeral in the titles of individual poems, but with VIII ceased that practice. He separated multiple sonnets on a page with a short rule, though not consistently. The side notes Lovecraft wrote on the manuscript during and following its composition are discussed in the commentary.

The draft manuscript comprises thirty-five sonnets, each heavily revised. There are cases of cancelled words, lines, and even stanzas. In one case, Lovecraft struck out two versions of an entire poem, only to write a third on another sheet, yet even that was heavily rewritten. He recorded the start and end dates of composition, along with certain milestone dates and number of lines completed to date. The manuscript surely did not circulate, as did the subsequent typescript. On the first page of the draft, Lovecraft noted individual poems earmarked for publication. (See Table 1 on page 129.) His notations, which are not thorough, date primarily to 1930. Some poems that appeared c. 1930–31 are not indicated as accepted, such as one to *L'Alouette* and several others to *Driftwind*. Lovecraft attempted to record appearances with greater precision on the typescript (item 3a), but that, too, has some omissions and oversights.

3. There is no fair typescript of the complete poem as we now know it. The following three items constitute what ultimately became the final state of the poem when R. H. Barlow attempted to publish it in 1936 and when it ultimately appeared in its entirety in *Beyond the Wall of Sleep* (1943).

3a. *Fungi from Yuggoth.* TMS, 11 pp. (with typed folios), typed early to mid-January 1930. Comprises sonnets I–XXXIII only. In the upper left corner of the first page is typed "H. P. Lovecraft, / ~~10 Barnes St.~~ [changed later in pen to] 66 College St. / Providence, R.I." Somewhat below Lovecraft wrote "Unpublished poetry." The note was meant to apply only to individual poems not marked as accepted, for as early as January 1930, some poems had been taken by several publications. In the upper right corner, Lovecraft has written "only copy. / Please return," and it appears that he long had only this one typed version of the poem, in danger of being lost during any of numerous loans. He prepared at least one other typescript, however, which he presented "To Saml. E. Loveman and Patrick McGrath, Esqrs., with the compliments & appreciation of the author— H. P. Lovecraft, May 22, 1930."[1]

3b. "Recapture." TMS, 1 p., dating to the time of item 1 above and slightly antedating item 3a. It is typed on the reverse side of a discarded sheet on which lines 45–46 of "The Outpost" ("None saw him leave, or come at dawn, / Nor does his flesh bear any mark") had been typed. In the upper left corner is typed "H. P. Lovecraft, / 10 Barnes St. / Providence, R.I." The entire address block was later cancelled, the number "12." written at the top of the page and circled (and apparently covering up an obliterated

---

1. http://www.sothebys.com/en/auctions/ecatalogue/2006/fine-books-and-manuscripts-including-a-private-collection-of-historical-hawaiiana-n08251/lot.70.html [October 2015; first posted 11 December 2006]. The ribbon copy typescript is described as consisting of "sonnets I to XXXII [*sic*] of *Fungi from Yuggoth*," 11 pages. HPL's own typescript contains eleven leaves with three sonnets to a page. It is not known if the Loveman/McGrath copy contains thirty-two or thirty-three poems. If XXXIII had been typed on the final leaf, that single page may have been lost.

"13."), and the number "XXXIV." inserted by hand before the title. In other words, c. 13 June 1936 Lovecraft (or R. H. Barlow) amended his file copy of "Recapture" to integrate it into *Fungi from Yuggoth*, following the last page of the original typescript. The typescript bears the author's name typed beneath the poem.

3c. "XXXV ~~XXXIV~~. Evening Star" and "XXXVI ~~XXXV~~. Continuity" (TMS, 1 p.), typed R. H. Barlow. When Lovecraft lent Barlow the main typescript of the poem as it existed c. 22 August 1934, he wrote in a letter: "Enclosed are the 'Fungi'—all, that is, which are typed. There are 2 more in MS. somewhere" (*OFF* 168); and "I'll dig up the longhand Fungi when I can—if you'll copy the two items not included in the typed version. Or maybe I'll have a burst of philanthropic energy & do it myself" (1 September 1934, *OFF* 173). It took Lovecraft three months to unearth the manuscript of the two poems (i.e., p. 20 of the draft): "As for the two remaining Fungi—here is the sheet, but it's very doubtful whether you can make anything of it. If you want to retain this scrawl, I'll have to ask for *two* typed copies . . . . one to lend & the other to keep on file. Better return the scrawl with the typed copies, so that I can make the proper corrections. Then I'll send it back" (*OFF* 191). The purpose of this lengthy exchange seems to have been for Barlow to make a duplicate typescript of the entire poem so that he could take Lovecraft's own typescript (and perhaps the handwritten draft) into his possession, since he habitually asked Lovecraft if he could have Lovecraft's manuscripts in exchange for newly typed copies.

It is uncertain why it took Barlow nearly four months to transcribe the final two poems (although admittedly, he may have found the draft to be somewhat daunting; see p. 104). Around 20 April 1935, Lovecraft wrote to Barlow: "Oh—by the way—thanks enormously for the typed copies of those two last 'fewngee'!" (*OFF* 250). Note that Lovecraft says "copies," presumably not referring to the poems, but to two separate sheets each bearing both. (See discussion of item 4.) Unlike the sonnets of the main *Fungi* typescript, these are typed double-spaced, with no break indicated between the octaves and sestets. The titles are not typed all caps (as Lovecraft did for all the other poems), but someone has double-underlined the titles to show they should be capped, or at least be treated in the same manner as the titles in 3a. Each is followed by a period, unlike the others, but even though the titles were corrected for capitalization, the periods were not cancelled. The positioning of the titles themselves does not follow Lovecraft's practice—that is, they (along with the Roman numerals) appear to be more or less centered, whereas the titles of the other poems are only indented the same uniform distance from the left margin. The two poems fill the sheet. Lovecraft otherwise easily fit three single-spaced sonnets to a sheet. Note also that the page had originally been numbered 12.

Lovecraft himself does not seem to have typed a personal copy of the two poems during the years following their original composition in January 1930. He was not averse to sending a neatly written fair copy of a poem for submittal to an *amateur* publication. He may have prepared at least one typescript of the two poems in the summer of 1932 to send to Walter M. Stevenson of the *Pioneer* for publication. Lovecraft's log of publication for *Fungi from Yuggoth* indicates only "Evening Star" as selected by *Pioneer*, although *Pioneer* also published "Continuity"—the penultimate and ultimate poems in the series. Still, the dashes on page 13, even though they consist of three hyphens, as was Lovecraft's practice, are followed by a space, which was not. This typed sheet is virtually identical to the last page of item 4 below. The manner of line spacing and the dashes are the same, but the titles of item 4 are all caps with no period.

It is uncertain what purpose the typed page was intended to serve. Both poems seem to have been typed at the same time. Lovecraft's name, which was hand-printed beneath the first poem, ultimately was erased, although it is printed again at the very bottom of the page, just between the ultimate line of text and a row of three asterisks indicating the conclusion of the typescript. Had the page been typed expressly for inclusion with *Fungi from Yuggoth*, why would he write his name on the sheet (twice!) when his byline already appears on the first page? The typed page had once been numbered "12." by hand, but that was erased, and the page was rendered as "13." at a later date, and the original typed numbering of the sonnets as XXXIV and XXXV was emended in ink (to account for the addition of "Recapture" as XXXIV).

4. *Fungi from Yuggoth.* TMS, 12 pp, typed by R. H. Barlow c. August 1934. At the time Barlow prepared this typescript (autumn 1934), "Recapture" still

was not part of the poem, and in fact the typescript initially did not include "Evening Star" and "Continuity." Unlike the page Barlow prepared later of the two poems, the format of *Fungi from Yuggoth* overall follows Lovecraft's method quite closely. Barlow probably prepared this copy in exchange for Lovecraft's original manuscript and typescript. He did not seem to have contemplated publishing the long poem at the time he made this copy, as he commenced typesetting the book only in December. But before then, Lovecraft lent Fred Anger and Louis Smith some typescript to consult for their own plan to publish the poem.

Clark Ashton Smith received a carbon of the poem from Barlow c. 12 September 1934. Smith's copy ends with "Harbour Whistles"; "Evening Star" and "Continuity" are not included. Barlow must had typed his copy from Lovecraft's own tattered typescript dating to 1930, which at the time still consisted only of thirty-three poems. Regarding the new copy, Lovecraft indicated to Barlow that "harbour" (XXXIII.2) was misspelled, as is apparent on p. 12 of Barlow's copy. Curiously, extant p. 12 of this copy includes not only "XXXIII. Harbour Whistles" but also "XXXIV. Evening Star" and "XXXV. Continuity." And yet Smith's carbon copy ended with "Harbour Whistles," the bottom two-thirds of the ultimate page being blank.

On Barlow's letter of "August 20-something [1934], Wed." (ms., JHL), Lovecraft listed errata to *Fungi from Yuggoth* (and also to Barlow's typescript of "Psychopompos"), which he returned with his letter of 7 September 1934 (*OFF* 175). Lovecraft listed 21 corrections, noting among them the omission of line 12 of "Alienation." Barlow made all the corrections by hand on his typescript, and also inserted line 7 of "The Book," which Lovecraft failed to notice as dropped. Smith had received his copy of the poem before these corrections could be made, but ultimately he was notified of the errors and he corrected his own copy.[2] The extant typescript by Barlow

2. Roy A. Squires offered CAS's carbon for sale c. 1973. In his catalogue, Squires noted that the TMS comprised "12 leaves of typewritten carbon copy; the first 33 sonnets (as in the first published collection; later collections include 3 additional). This copy was sent by Lovecraft to Clark Ashton Smith and contains 11 corrections penciled in Smith's hand, including 2 complete lines omitted by the typist" (*Beyond the Bibliographies* 4). Squires does not note as many corrections to be made as HPL had. He states: "The errors were indicated to Smith by letter, but whether Lovecraft was the typist is not known." In a letter to CAS c. 8 September 1934, HPL

seems to coincide with Smith's but with the important and puzzling exception noted above. Although both the JHL and Smith copies have 12 leaves, Smith's does not contain any more sonnets than thirty-three. How is it that both sets of typescripts—Barlow's and Smith's—do not contain the same number of poems? Close examination of Barlow's typescript shows that "Evening Star" and "Continuity" do not align exactly with the lines of "Harbour Whistles." Only after the transcript with thirty-three poems had been sent to Smith did Lovecraft and Barlow settle on the final disposition of the sonnets in *Fungi from Yuggoth*. Lovecraft finally must have conceded that no additional sonnets would be written. Thus, Barlow finally added the two poems long held aside in anticipation of further additions. But only after Barlow had *reinserted* the final page of the typescript into his typewriter and typed "XXXIV. Evening Star" and "XXXV. Continuity" did Lovecraft and he decide to bring "Recapture" into the body of the long poem. It appears that at that time, Barlow also added the dates of composition in the lower left corner of the sheet, beneath "Continuity."

This set of pages includes a typescript of "XXXIV. Recapture" (so typed) on a two-thirds sized sheet and another of "XXXV. Evening Star" and "XXXVI. Continuity" on a full letter-sized page. At the top of this latter page is typed "(This is a correct transcription.)" The typist must have been Barlow, for the overall form of the page is similar to that of item 3c above. The "I" in the number XXXIV that had originally been typed has been overtyped with a "V", and the original "V." has been erased and a new "." typed in, thus making "XXXV." Between the "V" and "." at the title of "Continuity" a typed "I" has been squeezed in. This page bears corrections and changes by Lovecraft, the corrected version of it being item 3c. Line 14 of "Evening Star" had "quivering," which Lovecraft corrected to "calling." This suggests that the page represents Barlow's first attempt to type the final

wrote: "Ar-Ech-Bei says he's sent you a carbon of his typescript of my Fungi. There are several errors—hence I'm enclosing an errata list which I hope you'll use in making corrections on the MS." The list does not survive. CAS acknowledged receipt of the carbon from RHB in a letter to him postmarked 12 September 1934 (ms., JHL). In a letter to CAS postmarked 28 October 1934 (ms., JHL), HPL wrote: "Thanks for spotting the two additional errors in Ar-E'ch-Bei's 'Fungi' text! I've corrected them in my copy, & shall advise the youthful acolyte of Krang to do likewise in his." The editor has not seen CAS's carbon typescript.

two poems from Lovecraft's original draft, and that he ultimately made a better copy to send Lovecraft, keeping the marked-up page for himself.

This shuffling of sonnets accounts for the handwritten notes in the form of dialogue on the last page of the top copy. It is not certain why the matter arose, but it seems that Barlow had suggested that "Recapture" be added to the sonnet sequence. Why? Because of thematic unity? For balance? (A thirty-sixth poem would fill an otherwise blank page at the end of the contemplated booklet, with one poem per page.) Barlow intended merely to place "Recapture" at the very end—the very simplest way to integrate the poem. But Lovecraft, who had long intended "Continuity" to conclude the series, instructed Barlow to "insert Recapture as XXXIV" ahead of "Evening Star," and so the numbering of the two concluding poems was revised to become XXXV and XXXVI. There is a corroborating note on the manuscript: "This makes a more logical *ending* than *Recapture,* which is appended as 36." In the end, Barlow acquiesced, for beneath Lovecraft's note he wrote: "You're right. Make it [i.e., "Continuity"] XXXVI." This exchange is confirmed in Lovecraft's letter to Barlow of 13 June 1936 (*OFF* 341–42).

The date "July 21, 1936" is written on leaf 7 of this set and "July 20, 1936 / completed" on leaf 8. These notes coincide with Barlow's printing of the sonnets thus labeled; i.e., "The Gardens of Yin" and "Azathoth." The last two lines of "The Lamp" are struck out, letter by letter with a virgule, the same as what Barlow did on his printed proof of the poem, as though for counting characters.

———————

5. The editor has seen posted on the Web an image of a typescript with the first three sonnets only (unnumbered) bearing a note signed by W. P[aul]. Cook that reads: "These poems were all to be in *Recluse,* scattered through the book as space permitted. Never printed. Some or all of these have been used elsewhere, I suppose." The typescript has the overarching title "*Fungi from Yuggoth* / by H. P. Lovecraft." The image is only of a single page and, as posted, is of too poor resolution to make out the text well. It appears that the titles may have been typed with the corresponding numerals, but they are very faint, suggesting that since they represented only a selection from the complete poem, the numbering was not

to be followed in typesetting the text. Did the document actually consist of *two* pages? Recall Lovecraft's marginal note on the draft of the poem: "Recluse I, II, III, VII, XII, XVIII." The six poems would easily fit on two pages. Lovecraft once told R. H. Barlow, who had the "rather bizarre notion of collecting everything which was to have gone into the 2nd Recluse," that he might "be interested to discover (from pencil notations imperfectly erased when the Recluse blew up) that the first 3 Fungi fall within that magic category."[3] It seems, then, that Cook may have in fact not taken VII, XII, and XVII as Lovecraft initially noted on the draft of the poem. Barlow had sought to obtain the items that were to appear in the second *Recluse* and must have asked Cook if he could have various items. The note on this particular document seems to have been directed to Barlow.

———————

6. *Fungi from Yuggoth.* TMS, 12 pp., typist seemingly was Lovecraft; date unknown. According to John Hay Library, this item constitutes two sets of carbon copies (each 12 pp.) made by R. H. Barlow, in an envelope, addressed to Barlow, hand-cancelled, with no postmark, at Providence. (What became of the ribbon copy?) It does not make sense that these carbons would be addressed *to* Barlow if they were *by* Barlow. The last line of page 1 of one set runs partially off the sheet—as though the typist had been trying to type two or three carbons at one time, and the last sheet slipped when being fed through the typewriter. The em-dashes throughout consist of only two hyphens, whereas Lovecraft characteristically used three. Note that this fair copy contains 35 numbered sonnets. It appears to have been typed c. 1935, for the numbers of the sonnets are typed without the revision of "Evening Star" and "Continuity" in the case of 3a and 4 above.

———————

7. Known fair copies of individual poems include "Background" and "Mirage" at JHL; another copy of "Background" (provenance unknown);[4] "Homecoming" at the University of North Texas Music Library among the

———

3. HPL to RHB, 22 August 1934, *OFF* 168.
4. http://chrisperridas.blogspot.com/2008/06/rare-autographed-item-in-lovecrafts.html [October 2015]

Willis Conover papers (see p. 21 of *Lovecraft at Last*, constituting Lovecraft's submittal for publication in the *Science-Fantasy Correspondent*); "Continuity" in Lovecraft's letter to J. Vernon Shea of 8–22 November 1933 (ms., JHL); "Recapture" in Lovecraft's letter to Clark Ashton Smith of 19 November 1929. There likely are others, since late in life Lovecraft sent individual poems to various small magazines for publication—the handwritten copy of "Homecoming" on a file card for Willis Conover is a prime example.

---

8. The editor has a photocopy (provenance unknown) of a typescript of *Fungi from Yuggoth* (11 pp., I–XXXIII only) with an address sticker on the first and last pages stating "WILLIAM H. EVANS / 233 Sheldon Ave. / AMES, IOWA." The typist is unknown. There are various handwritten corrections, but the typist failed to note that line 4 was omitted from "Harbour Whistles." This document presumably served as the copy text, albeit corrected, of Evans's FAPA [Fantasy Amateur Press Association] submission of *Fungi from Yuggoth* (also I–XXXIII only). In the FAPA appearance, lines 6 and 7 of "Expectancy" are conflated.

The copy-text for this edition of *Fungi from Yuggoth* is Lovecraft's typescript (all elements of item 3 above) at John Hay Library. All textual variants in published appearances are the result of publishers' emendations or misprints—none can be ascribed to later revision by Lovecraft. Minor emendations made for the purpose of consistency are noted where appropriate (e.g., the typescript uses *show* but Lovecraft otherwise preferred and used *shew*). The publications listed below represent major appearances of the individual sonnets: during Lovecraft's lifetime, shortly after his death (because some items were in the hands of publishers at the time), all first appearances, appearances in major collections, and so on.

The following publications were not consulted in the collation of texts: *Acolyte*, *Phantagraph* (1941), *Drab*, *Stars*, *Dark of the Moon* (1947), *Collected Poems* (1963), *Fungi from Yuggoth and Other Poems* (1971), *Mirage*, reprints in *Weird Tales* (post-1937), the Canadian *Weird Tales*, *The* [sic] *Fungi from Yuggoth* (1977), *Fungi from Yuggoth* (1982), *The Illustrated Fungi from Yug-*

goth (1983), all anthology appearances (save *Harvest*), and other less important items. Likewise, the various typed copies of the poem by R. H. Barlow and others were not consulted.

A	*L'Alouette* (1)
B	*Beyond the Wall of Sleep* (36)
C	*Causerie* (1)
DN	[Cambridge, MD] *Democrat and News* (4)
D	*Driftwind* (10)
EE	editor's emendation
FF	*Fantasy Fan* (4)
FY	*Fungi from Yuggoth* (1943) (33)
G	*Galleon* (1)
H	*Harvest* (1)
HPL	*HPL* (5)
II	*Interesting Items* (2)
L	*Lovecrafter* (1)
LaL	*Lovecraft at Last* (1)
P	*Pioneer* (2)
Ph	*Phantagraph* (5; does not include that of 1941)
PJ	*Providence Journal* (5)
R	*Ripples from Lake Champlain* (1)
SC	*Science-Fantasy Correspondent* (1)
SF	*Silver Fern* (1)
SFB	*Science Fiction Bard* (1)
WT	*Weird Tales* (only those 11 [including "Recapture"] that appeared in Lovecraft's lifetime, of 30 total)

I. The Book   *FF, D, FY, B*

Title: I.] ~:— *D*
3   seas,] ~∧ *D*
6   shewed] EE; showed TMS, *FF, D, FY, B*
No break between ll. 8 and 9 in *D*.
10   through] thru *D*
12   mon∫trous] montrose *FY*
         knew.] ~ , *FF, FY;* ~; *D*

II. Pursuit   *FF, FY, B*

3   harbour] harbor *FY*
5   Dull,] ~∧ *FY*
11   worlds] words *FY*

III. The Key   *FF, FY, B*

2   more,] ~∧ *B*
8   demesnes] desmesnes *FY*
12   memories] Memories *B*

IV. Recognition   *D, FY, B*

Title: IV.] *Omitted in D*
5   same—] ~ ... *D*
         an] and *FY*
11   ∫trange,] ~∧ *D, FY*
12   voids—] *B;* ~,— TMS; ~; *D*
14   late] ~ , *FY*
         I!] ~∧ *D, FY*

V. Homecoming   *FF, LaL, SC, HPL, DN, FY, B*

Title: V.] *Omitted in LaL, SC, HPL, DN*
2   pale,] ~∧ *FY*
         shadowy] shadow- *FF*
         half-]~∧ *FY*

13   night:] ~. *FY*

14   home",] home," *FF, DN, FY, SC, B*

VI. The Lamp   *D, FY, B*

Title: VI.] *Omitted in D*

2   chiselled] chiseled *D;* chisselled *FY*

3   frightened] frightening *FY*

7   obscurely-] EE; cf. XXXIII.6; ~^ TMS, *D, FY, B*
      scroll,] ~^ *FY*

10   us] ~, *FY*

13   great] Great *FY*
      God! . . .] EE; ~!...... TMS; ~ !— *D*
      . . . But] —But *D;* —but *FY*

VII. Zaman's Hill   *D, FY, B*

Title: VII.] *Omitted in D*

1   The] A *FY*

3   tall,] ~^ *D*

4   highway] ~'s *FY*
      bend.] ~^ *D*

6   slope—] ~: *D*

11   ſtare—] ~.... *D*

14   eyes,] ~^ *FY*

VIII. The Port   *D, FY, B*

Title: VIII.] *Omitted in D*

6   bleach,] ~; *FY*

9   echoing] EE; Echoing TMS, *D, FY, B*

10   times. But] ~, ~ *B*

12   Whence] Where *D*
      tomb!] ~. *FY*

IX. The Courtyard   *WT, FY, B*

Title: IX.] 1. *WT*

2   ancient,] ~^ *FY*
6   half-] ~^ *FY*
14   head!] ~. *FY*
In *WT*, ll. 2, 3, 5, 8, 10, and 12 are indented.

X. The Pigeon-Flyers   *R, DN, FY, B*

Title: X.] *Omitted in DN*
2   viscous] viscious *R;* viscuous *DN*
5   fires] flares *FY*
6   roofs] ~, *FY*
7   sky] ~, *FY*
10   of space] *Omitted in FY*
        Outside—] **outside**— *DN;* Outside^ *FY*
12   Thog] Thog *FY*
14   glimpsed] glimped *DN*

XI. The Well   *PJ, Ph, FY, B*

Title: XI.] *Omitted in PJ, Ph*
5   crazy,] ~^ *FY*
6   him] ~ up *FY*
7   -mouth] *Omitted in FY*

XII. The Howler   *D, FY, B*

Title: XII.] *Omitted in D*
1   Briggs'] ~^ *D*
2   through] thru *D*
3   seventeen-four] seventy-four *D*
5   disobeyed,] ~^ *D*
10   howls,] ~^ *D*
11   through] thru *D*
13   glimpsed—] ~...... *D.*
        place,] ~^ *D*

XIII. Hesperia   *WT, FY, B*

Title: XIII.] 3. *WT*
4   splendours] splendors *WT*
14   these] those *FY*
In *WT,* ll. 2, 3, 5, 8, 10, 11, 13, and 14 are indented.

XIV. Star-Winds   *WT, FY, B*

Title: XIV.] 2. *WT*
4   shewing] EE; showing TMS, *WT, FY, B*
6   chimney-] ~∧ *FY*
          grace,] ~∧ *B*
13   us] me *FY*
14   away!] ~. *FY*
In *WT,* ll. 2, 3, 5, 8, 10, 11, 13, and 14 are indented.

XV. Antarktos   *WT, FY, B*

Title: XV.] 4. *WT*
4   aeons] eons *WT*
10   mound] mould *FY*
12   bide] hide *FY, B*
13   shew] EE; show TMS, *WT, FY, B*
In *WT,* ll. 2, 4, 6, 8, 10, and 12 are indented.

XVI. The Window   *D, FY, B*

Title: XVI.] *Omitted in D*
1   outthrown] out-thrown *D*
14   wild] wide *D*

XVII. A Memory   *DN, FY, B*

Title: XXVI.] *Omitted in DN*
2   half-] ~∧ *FY*
          night,] ~∧ *DN*
10   came,] ~; *FY*

XVIII. The Gardens of Yin   *D, FY, B*

Title: XVIII.] *Omitted in D*
1   that] the *D*
2   towers,] ~∧ *D*
3   gardens,] ~∧ *D*
6   lotos] lotus *D, FY, B*
8   cherry-] ~∧ *D*
13   hurried—]~, *D*

XIX. The Bells   *WT, FY, B*

Title: XIX.] 5. *WT*
3   ſteeple] ſteeples *FY*
10   rain] rains *B*
In *WT*, ll. 2, 3, 5, 8, 10, and 12 are indented.

XX. Night-Gaunts   *PJ, II, Ph, SFB, HPL, DN, FY, B*

Title: XX.] *Omitted in PJ, Ph, SFB, HPL, DN*
       Night-] ~∧ *II, HPL;* ~-[space] *SFB*
1   crypt] Crypt *II*
       tell,] ~. *II*
2   rubbery] rub ery *SFB* (likely a failure of the missing "b" to ink)
       things,] ~: *Ph, HPL;* ~; *II, SFB, FY*
3   horned,] ~∧ *II*
       membraneous] membranous *FY*
4   hell.] ~, *II*
5   north wind's] northwind's *Ph, HPL*
       swell,] ~. *DN;* ~∧ *B*
6   clutch] touch *DN*
7   voyagings] ~, *DN*
8   grey] gray *Ph,*
12   shoggoths] shaggoths *FY*
       sleep.] ~; *II;* ~∧ *Ph*
13   oh!] ho! *B*
       If] if *Ph, SFB, HPL*

only they would] they would only *FY*

In *PJ*, ll. 2, 3, 6, 7, 10, 11, 13, and 14 are indented.

XXI. Nyarlathotep   *WT, FY, B*

Title: XXI.] 6. *WT*

13   to mould] *Omitted in FY*

        mould] mold *WT*

In *WT*, ll. 2, 3, 5, 8, 10, 11, 13, and 14 are indented.

XXII. Azathoth   *WT, FY, B*

Title: XXII.] 7. *WT*

1   daemon] dæmon *WT*

8   ſtreams] ſtream *FY* [faulty impression?]

9   high,] ~∧ *FY*

11   flow] flew *FY*

13   Messenger,"] *FY, B;* ~", TMS]

        daemon] dæmon *WT*

In *WT*, ll. 2, 4, 6, 8, 10, and 12 are indented.

XXIII. Mirage   *WT, FY, B*

Title: XXIII.] 8. *WT*

10   wheeled,] ~; *FY*

12   ſtill.] ~, *FY*

14   be,] ~∧ *FY*

In *WT*, ll. 2, 3, 6, 7, 10, and 12 are indented.

XXIV. The Canal   *D, H, FY, B*

Title: XXIV.] *Omitted in D, H*

2   tall,] ~∧ *D, H*

3   channel,] ~; *FY*

4   things] ~, *D*

        whence] where *FY*

5   half-] ~∧ *D, H*

9   one] *Omitted in B*

In H there is a line of space between ll. 12 and 13.
14   day.] ~.. *FY*; clay. *B*

XXV. St. Toad's   *FY, B*

10   shriek:] ~^ *FY*
12   paused,] ~; *FY*
        fear:] ~, *FY*
14   black] vaſt *FY*

XXVI. The Familiars   *D, FY, B*

Title: XXVI.] *Omitted in D*
1   John] —John (HPL's change on a proof of Dragon-Fly Press ed.)
        town,] ~^ *D*

XXVII. The Elder Pharos   *WT, FY, B*

Title: XXVII.] 9. *WT*
4   far] ~, *WT*
In *WT*, ll. 2, 3, 6, 7, 10, and 12 are indented.

XXVIII. Expectancy   *FY, B*

6–7   *In FY conflated to a single line:* As of vaſt adventures, uncorporeal,
8   shew] EE; show TMS
9   sunsets] ~, *FY*
13   though] through *FY*

XXIX. Nostalgia   *PJ, Ph, HPL, FY, B*

Title: XXIX.] Omitted form *PJ, Ph, HPL*
        "Noſtalgia" *Ph*
7   temple-] ~^ *PJ, Ph, HPL, FY*
        interlaced] overlaced *Ph, HPL*
8   shew.] EE; show. TMS, *PJ, Ph, HPL, FY, B*
13   Yet] ~, *PJ, Ph, HPL*

XXX. Background   *PJ, II, G, L, FY, B*

Title: XXX.] *Omitted in PJ, G, L*
        Background] A Sonnet *L*
2   town,] ~. *II*
4   harbour] harbor *G, L, FY*
5   share] where *FY*
6   window-] ~^ *II, FY*
7   vanes—] ~ , *II;* vans— *L;* vines *FY*
9   treasures,] ~^ *G, L*
10   loose] lose *II*
13   thongs] things *PJ;* throngs, *FY*

XXXI. The Dweller   *PJ, Ph, HPL, FY, B*

Title: XXXI.] *Omitted in PJ, Ph, HPL*
2   knows] knew *HPL;* know *FY*
        that mound,] the ground, *FY*
4   blocks] ~ , *FY*
5   foundation-] ~^ *HPL, FY*
6   shew] EE; show TMS, *PJ, Ph, HPL, FY, B*
13   path—] ~. . . *HPL*

XXXII. Alienation   *WT, FY, B*

Title: XXXII.] 10. *WT*
8   behind.] beyond *FY*
12   False,] ~^ *B*
14   which] whom *FY*
In *WT,* ll. 2, 3, 5, 6, 7, 10, 11, 13, and 14 are indented.

XXXIII. Harbour Whistles   *SF, A, Ph, HPL, FY, B*

Title: XXXIII.] *Omitted in SF, A, Ph, HPL*
        Harbour] Harbor *FY*
2   harbour] harbor *FY*
3   *Entire line omitted in FY*

ports,] parts, *SF, A*

white,] wide, *SF, A*

4   choirs.]~, *SF, A, FY*

5   unknown,] ~; *FY*

6   obscurely-] ~^ *FY*

force] farce *SF, A*

8   Fused] Fuse *FY*

XXXIV. Recapture   [*WT*], *B*

Entire poem omitted from FY

Title: XXXIV.] Not numbered in *WT*. The number was not assigned to the poem until after its firſt appearance in *WT*.

2   grey] gray *WT*

mould,] mold, *WT*

XXXV. Evening Star   *P, B*

Entire poem omitted from FY

Title: XXXV.] *Omitted in P*

3   thin] this *P*

5   lone] love- *P*

7   evening ſtar] Evening Star *P*

ſtar—] ~, *B*

thousandfold] thousand fold *P*

9   ſtrange] ſtrayed *P*

on] in *P*

11   gardens;] ~: *P*

14   loſt] laſt *P*

In *P* there is no break between the octave and the ſeſtet.

XXXVI. Continuity   *P, C, B*

Entire poem omitted from FY

Title: XXXVI.] *Omitted in P, C*

3   aether] ether *P*

7   harbouring] harboring *P*

12	than this] *Omitted in P*
13	feel I] ~ that ~ P
14	fixt] fixed P

In *P* there is no break between the octave and the sestet.

The Musical Compositions of Harold S. Farnese

MIRAGE

Poem by H. P. Lovecraft

Music by Harold Farnese, op. 52 no. 1.

I do not know if it ev-er ex-ist-ed That lost world floating dimly on life's stream— And yet I see it oft-en vi - o-let mist-ed And shim ring at the back of some vague dream. There were strange tow- ers and cur - ious lap- ping riv- ers

while on a windswept hill There stands a village, an-cis-ent and white

sleep - led, With eve-ning chimes for which I list-en still.

I do not know what land it is - or dare Ask when or why I was

or will be there

The Elder Pharos

Poem by
H. P. Lovecraft

Music by
Harold Farnese Op.22 no.2.

From Leng where rock-y peaks climb bleak and bare Un-der cold stars ob-scure to human sight. There shoots at dusk a sin-gle beam of light Whose far blue rays make shepherds whine in

Appendix E: Musical Compositions

prayer They say tho' none has been there, that it comes Out of a

pha-ros in a tow'r of stone. Where the last Eld-er One

lives on a-lone__ Talk-ing to Cha-os with the beat of drums.

The thing they whisper wears a silk-en mask of yel-low whose queer folds ap-pear to hide__

: 3 :

Appendix E: Musical Compositions

Bibliography

Fungi from Yuggoth: Appearances of Individual Poems

    I. "The Book." *Fantasy Fan* 2, No. 2 (October 1934): 24. *Driftwind* 11, No. 9 (April 1937): 342.

    II. "Pursuit." *Fantasy Fan* 2, No. 2 (October 1934): 24.

    III. "The Key." *Fantasy Fan* 2, No. 5 (January 1935): 72.

    IV. "Recognition." *Driftwind* 11, No. 5 (December 1936): 180.

    V. "Homecoming." *Fantasy Fan* 2, No. 5 (January 1935): 72. *Science-Fantasy Correspondent* 1, No. 1 (November–December 1936): 24. [Cambridge, MD] *Democrat & News* (8 July 1937). *Weird Tales* 37, No. 5 (May 1944): 52–53. *Weird Tales* (Canadian) 38, No. 3 (January 1946): 56.

    VI. "The Lamp." *Driftwind* 5, No. 5 (March 1931): 16. *Weird Tales* 33, No. 2 (February 1939): 151.

    VII. "Zaman's Hill." *Driftwind* 9, No. 4 (October 1934): 125. *Weird Tales* 33, No. 2 (February 1939): 151.

    VIII. "The Port." *Driftwind* 5, No. 3 (November 1930): 36. *Weird Tales* 39, No. 7 (September 1946): 65. *Weird Tales* (Canadian) 38, No. 4 (November 1946): 40.

    IX. "The Courtyard." *Weird Tales* 16, No. 3 (September 1930): 322 [as No. 1].

    X. "The Pigeon-Flyers." *Ripples from Lake Champlain* 2, No. 4 (Spring 1932): 31. [Cambridge, MD] *Democrat & News* (8 July 1937). *Weird Tales* 39, No. 9 (January 1947): 96. *Weird Tales* (Canadian) 38, No. 4 [*sic*] (March 1947): 110.

    XI. "The Well." *Providence Journal* 102, No. 116 (14 May 1930): 15. *Phantagraph* 6, No. 3 (July 1937): [1]. *Weird Tales* 37, No. 5 (May 1944): 53. *Crypt of Cthulhu* No. 20 (Eastertide 1984): 8 (as "Two Discarded Drafts of 'The Well'").

XII. "The Howler." *Driftwind* 7, No. 3 (November 1932): 100. *Weird Tales* 34, No. 1 (June–July 1939): 66.

XIII. "Hesperia." *Weird Tales* 16, No. 4 (October 1930): 464 [as No. 3].

XIV. "Star-Winds." *Weird Tales* 16, No. 3 (September 1930): 322 [as No. 2].

XV. "Antarktos." *Weird Tales* 16, No. 5 (November 1930): 692 [as No. 4]. In *Antarktos*. Warren, OH: Fantome Press, 1977. [5].

XVI. "The Window." *Driftwind* 5 (April 1931 [special issue]): 15. *Weird Tales* 37, No. 5 (May 1944): 53. *Weird Tales* (Canadian) 38, No. 3 (September 1945): 75. *Hi-Lite* [Mannheim Township High School, Nettsville, PA] (30 October 1946).

XVII. "A Memory." [Cambridge, MD] *Democrat & News* (8 July 1937). *Weird Tales* 39, No. 10 (March 1947): 69. *Weird Tales* (Canadian) 38, No. 3 (January 1946): 65.

XVIII. "The Gardens of Yin." *Driftwind* 6, No. 5 (March 1932): 34. *Weird Tales* 34, No. 2 (August 1939): 151.

XIX. "The Bells." *Weird Tales* 16, No. 6 (December 1930): 798 (as No. 5).

XX. "Night-Gaunts." *Providence Journal* 102, No. 73 (26 March 1930): 15. *Interesting Items* No. 605 (November 1934): [6] (as "Night Gaunts"). *Phantagraph* 4, No. 3 ([June] 1936): [8]. *Science Fiction Bard* 1, No. 1 (May 1937): 2–3. [Cambridge, MD] *Democrat & News* (8 July 1937). *Weird Tales* 34, No. 6 (December 1939): 59. *Drab* 1, No. 2 (n.d.) [2].

XXI. "Nyarlathotep." *Weird Tales* 17, No. 1 (January 1931): 12 (as No. 6).

XXII. "Azathoth." *Weird Tales* 17, No. 1 (January 1931): 12 (as No. 7).

XXIII. "Mirage." *Weird Tales* 17, No. 2 (February–March 1931): 175 (as No. 8). *Mirage* 1, No. 5 (Summer 1962): 3.

XXIV "The Canal." *Driftwind* 6, No. 5 (March 1932): 34. *Weird Tales* 31, No. 1 (January 1938): 20. *Weird Tales* 47, No. 1 (Summer 1973): 96.

XXV. "St. Toad's." *Weird Tales* 37, No. 5 (May 1944): 52. *Weird Tales* (Canadian) 38, No. 3 (September 1945): 105 (as by "J. H. Brownlow," a house name).

XXVI. "The Familiars." *Driftwind* 5, No. 1 (July 1930): 35. *Weird Tales* 39, No. 9 (January 1947): 96. *Weird Tales* (Canadian) 38, No. 4 [*sic*] (March 1947): 59.

XXVII. "The Elder Pharos." *Weird Tales* 17, No. 2 (February–March 1931): 175 (as No. 9).

XXVIII. "Expectancy." [Never periodically published.]

XXIX. "Nostalgia." *Providence Journal* 102, No. 61 (12 March 1930): 15. *Phantagraph* 4, No. 4 (July 1936): [1]. *Stars* (December [1940]–January 1941): 2.

XXX. "Background." *Providence Journal* 102, No. 91 (16 April 1930): 13. *Interesting Items* No. 592 (September 1932): [1]. *Galleon* 1, No. 4 (May–June 1935): 8. *Lovecrafter* 47, No. 1 (20 August 1936): [1] (as "A Sonnet"; in fact, the only appearance of the publication, intended as a birthday present for HPL [actually his forty-sixth]).

XXXI. "The Dweller." *Providence Journal* 102, No. 110 (7 May 1930): 15. *Phantagraph* 4, No. 2 (November–December 1935): [3]. *Weird Tales* 35, No. 2 (March 1940): 20. *Weird Fiction Times* No. 44 (February 1976): 29.

XXXII. "Alienation." *Weird Tales* 17, No. 3 (April–May 1931): 374 (as No. 10).

XXXIII. "Harbour Whistles." *Silver Fern* 1, No. 5 (May 1930): [1]. *L'Alouette* 3, No. 6 (September–October 1930): 161. *Phantagraph* 5, No. 2 (November 1936): [1]. *Weird Tales* 33, No. 5 (May 1939): 134. [*Note:* Arkham House transcript 34.107 contains the text of "Harbour Whistles" with the following note: "from l'Alouette [*sic*]: a magazine of verse. / Reprinted in Threads in Tapestry—1936." *Threads in Tapestry*, compiled and edited by Rachel Hall, Marcia A. Taylor, Charles A. A. Parker (Medford, MA: C. A. A. Parker), appeared in editions for 1934 and 1935. No edition for 1936 has been found.]

XXXIV. "Recapture." *Weird Tales* 15, No. 5 (May 1930): 693. *Weird Tales* 39, No. 3 (January 1946): 37. *Weird Tales* (Canadian) 38, No. 4 (March 1946): 78.

XXXV. "Evening Star." *Pioneer* 2, No. 4 (Autumn 1932): 16. *Weird Tales* 37, No. 5 (May 1944): 52. *Weird Tales* (Canadian) 38, No. 3 (July 1945): 100.

XXXVI. "Continuity." *Pioneer* 2, No. 2 [i.e., 3] (Summer 1932): 6. *Causerie* (February 1936): [1]. *Phantagraph* 9, No. 1 (May–June 1941): 7. *Acolyte* 1, No. 4 (Summer 1943): 6. *Weird Tales* 39, No. 10 (March 1947): 69. *Weird Tales* (Canadian) 38, No. 4 [*sic*] (July 1947): 110.

Fungi from Yuggoth: Book Publications

Fungi from Yuggoth. Circulated by William H. Evans through the Fantasy Amateur Press Association [FAPA], June 1943; probably fewer than 75 copies. *Contains: Fungi from Yuggoth* (I–XXXIII only).

Beyond the Wall of Sleep. Sauk City, WI: Arkham House, 1943. *Contains: Fungi from Yuggoth* ([395]–407). The first appearance of the entire poem, as finally established by HPL in 1936.

Collected Poems. Sauk City, WI: Arkham House, 1963. *Contains: Fungi from Yuggoth* ([107]–34).

Fungi from Yuggoth and Other Poems. New York: Ballantine Books, February 1971. *Contains: Fungi from Yuggoth* ([109]–38). Reprint, with slight differences, of *Collected Poems.*

The [*sic*] *Fungi from Yuggoth.* West Warwick, RI: Necronomicon Press, 1977.

Fungi from Yuggoth. West Warwick, RI: Necronomicon Press, 1982. 14 pp.

The Illustrated Fungi from Yuggoth. Illustrated by Robert Kellough. Madison, WI: Dream House, 1983. 51 pp. In this edition, the poems are not numbered and some are transposed as follows to accommodate the illustrations: "The Lamp"/"Homecoming"; "Azathoth"/"Nyarlathotep"; "A Memory"/"The Window."

HPL. Published by Corwin F. Stickney (Bellville, NJ), 1937. No printing information appears in the booklet. It was announced in the *Amateur Correspondent* for May/June 1937, and so must have appeared c. summer. Twenty-five copies were printed and given free to subscribers to Stickney's *Amateur Correspondent. Contains:* "Homecoming" [7], "Nostalgia" [9], "Night Gaunts" [*sic*] [11], "The Dweller" [13], and "Harbour Whistles" [15]. The poems, which all appeared initially in the *Providence Journal,* had been accepted for *Science-Fantasy Correspondent* and *Phantagraph.*

Coates, Walter John, ed. *Harvest: A Sheaf of Poems from* Driftwind: *April, 1926 to May, 1933.* North Montpelier, VT: Driftwind Press, May 1933. *Contains:* "The Canal" (33).

Coblentz, Stanton A., ed. *Unseen Wings: The Living Poetry of Man's Immortality.* New York: Beechhurst Press, 1949. *Contains:* "Continuity" and "A Memory" (229).

Derleth, August. *H. P. L.: A Memoir.* New York: Ben Abramson, 1945. *Contains:* "The Window" (110–11).

Derleth, August, ed. *Dark of the Moon: Poems of Fantasy and the Macabre.* Sauk City, WI: Arkham House, 1947; Freeport, NY: Books for Libraries Press, 1969. *Contains: Fungi from Yuggoth* (299–316).

Docherty, Chris J., A. Langley Searles, and Kenneth W. Faig, Jr. *Devonshire Ancestry of Howard Phillips Lovecraft.* Glenview, IL: Moshassuck Press, 2003.

Goodstone, Tony, ed. *The Pulps: Fifty Years of American Pop Culture.* New York: Bonanza Books, [1970]; New York: Chelsea House, 1976, 1980. *Contains:* "Continuity" and "The Gardens of Yin" (200 [1980: 164]).

Haining, Peter, ed. *Weird Tales: A Facsimile of the World's Most Famous Fantasy Magazine.* Jersey, UK: Neville Spearman, 1976. *Contains:* "The Familiars" and "The Pigeon-Flyers" (208).

———. *Weird Tales: Volume 2.* [Cover reads *More Weird Tales.*] London: Sphere, 1978. *Contains:* "The Familiars" (161) and "The Pigeon-Flyers" (163).

Hoke, Helen, ed. *Weirdies, Weirdies, Weirdies.* London: Franklin Watts, 1973, 1975. *Contains:* "The Howler" (110); "Night-Gaunts" (as "The Night Crawlers") (109).

Lovecraft, H. P. *Dreams and Fancies.* Sauk City, WI: Arkham House, 1962. *Contains:* "Recapture" in a letter to Clark Ashton Smith (29); and "Night-Gaunts" (56).

Lovecraft, H. P., and Willis Conover. *Lovecraft at Last.* Arlington, VA: Carrollton-Clark, 1975; New York: Cooper Square Press, 2002. *Contains:* "Homecoming" (facsimile reproduction of holograph ms.) (21).

Lucie-Smith, Edward, ed. *Holding Your Eight Hands: An Anthology of Science Fiction Verse.* Garden City, NY: Doubleday, 1969; London: Rapp & Whiting, 1970. *Contains:* "Nyarlathotep" (59) and "Harbour Whistles" (60).

Pepper, Elizabeth, and John Wilcock, ed. *The Witches' Almanac: Aries 1972–Pisces 1973.* New York: Grosset & Dunlap, 1973. *Contains:* "Expectancy" (5).

Price, Robert M. ed. *The Antarktos Cycle.* Oakland, CA: Chaosium, 1999. *Contains:* "Antarktos" (1).

———. *The Nyarlathotep Cycle.* Oakland, CA: Chaosium, 1997. *Contains:* "Nyarlathotep" (17).

Vaughan, Ralph E., ed. *Lost Lands.* San Diego: Ralph E. Vaughan, [1983]. *Contains:* "Antarktos" (6).

Wollheim, Donald A., ed. *Avon Fantasy Reader No. 1.* New York: Avon, 1947. *Contains:* "Nostalgia" (115).

———. *The Macabre Reader.* New York: Ace, 1959; London: Brown, Watson (Digit Books), [1960]. *Contains:* "Night-Gaunts" (47 [40]) and "The Dweller" (223 [188]).

———. *Operation Phantasy.* Rego Park, NY: Phantagraph Press, 1967. *Contains:* "Harbour Whistles" (15).

[Unsigned, ed.] *American Poetry: The Twentieth Century.* New York: Library of America, 2000. *Contains:* "Alienation" and "The Well" (1.825).

Audio Recordings of *Fungi from Yuggoth*

Fungi from Yuggoth: A Sonnet Cycle. Read by John Arthur, music by Mike Olson, directed by Lawrence A. Russo. An audio recording, accompanied with music. Nampa, ID: Fedogan & Bremer, 2015. Released in 1987 on cassette; this recording is remastered for CD and contains, along with Lovecraft's poem, Harold S. Farnese's music for "Mirage" and "The Elder Pharos," along with other compositions.

H. P. Lovecraft's Fungi from Yuggoth and Other Poems. Read by William Hart, scored by Graham Plowman. Nampa, ID: Fedogan & Bremer, 2016. An audio recording, accompanied with music.

Works by H. P. Lovecraft

The Ancient Track: Complete Poetical Works. Ed. S. T. Joshi. 2nd ed. New York: Hippocampus Press, 2013. *Contains:* "The Ancient Track" (78–80), "The East India Brick Row" (308–09), *Fungi from Yuggoth* (80–95), "The Messenger" (80), "The Outpost" (77–79), "Sonnet Study" (197–98).

The Annotated Supernatural Horror in Literature. Ed. S. T. Joshi. 2nd ed. New York: Hippocampus Press, 2012.

Beyond the Wall of Sleep. Collected by August Derleth and Donald Wandrei. Sauk City, WI: Arkham House, 1943.

Collected Essays. 5 volumes. Ed. S. T. Joshi. New York: Hippocampus Press, 2004–06.

Collected Fiction: A Variorum Edition. 4 volumes. Ed. S. T. Joshi. New York: Hippocampus Press, 2015–16 (vols. 1–4); 2022 (expanded vol 4).

Collected Poems. [Ed. Auguſt Derleth.] Sauk City, WI: Arkham House, 1963.

Commonplace Book. 2 volumes. Ed. David E. Schultz. Weſt Warwick, RI: Necronomicon Press, 1987.

The Dark Brotherhood and Other Pieces. [Ed. Auguſt Derleth.] Sauk City, WI: Arkham House, 1966.

Dawnward Spire, Lonely Hill: The Letters of H. P. Lovecraft and Clark Ashton Smith. Ed. David E. Schultz and S. T. Joshi. New York: Hippocampus Press, 2017.

Dreams and Fancies. [Ed. August Derleth.] Sauk City, WI: Arkham House, 1962.

Essential Solitude: The Letters of H. P. Lovecraft and Auguſt Derleth. 2 volumes. Ed. David E. Schultz and S. T. Joshi. New York: Hippocampus Press, 2008.

Fungi from Yuggoth. [Ed. S. T. Joshi.] Weſt Warwick, RI: Necronomicon Press, 1982. Differs from the earlier Necronomicon Press edition, *The* [*sic*] *Fungi from Yuggoth* (1977), which contains numerous errors.

Letters with Donald and Howard Wandrei and to Emil Petaja. Ed. S. T. Joshi and David E. Schultz. New York: Hippocampus Press, 2019.

Letters to Alfred Galpin and Others. Ed. S. T. Joshi and David E. Schultz. New York: Hippocampus Press, 2020.

Letters to C. L. Moore and Others. Ed. David E. Schultz and S. T. Joshi. New York: Hippocampus Press, 2017.

Letters to Elizabeth Toldridge and Anne Tillery Renshaw. Ed. David E. Schultz and S. T. Joshi. New York: Hippocampus Press, 2014.

Letters to F. Lee Baldwin, Duane W. Rimel, and Nils Frome. Ed. David E. Schultz and S. T. Joshi. New York: Hippocampus Press, 2016.

Letters to Family and Family Friends. Ed. S. T. Joshi and David E. Schultz. New York: Hippocampus Press, 2020.

"Letters to Farnsworth Wright." Ed. S. T. Joshi and David E. Schultz. *Lovecraft Annual* 8 (2015): 5–59.

Letters to J. Vernon Shea, Carl F. Strauch, and Lee McBride White. Ed. S. T. Joshi and David E. Schultz. New York: Hippocampus Press, 2016.

Letters to James F. Morton. Ed. David E. Schultz and S. T. Joshi. New York: Hippocampus Press, 2011.

Letters to Maurice W. Moe and Others. Ed. David E. Schultz and S. T. Joshi. New York: Hippocampus Press, 2018.

Letters to Rheinhart Kleiner and Others. Ed. S. T. Joshi and David E. Schultz. New York: Hippocampus Press, 2020.

Letters to Robert Bloch and Others. Ed. David E. Schultz and S. T. Joshi. New York: Hippocampus Press, 2015.

Lovecraft at Last. By H. P. Lovecraft and Willis Conover, Jr. Arlington VA: Carrollton-Clark, 1975. Rpt. with new introduction by S. T. Joshi, New York: Cooper Square Press, 2002.

A Means to Freedom: Letters of H. P. Lovecraft and Robert E. Howard. 2 volumes. Ed. S. T. Joshi, David E. Schultz, and Rusty Burke. New York: Hippocampus Press, 2009.

Miscellaneous Letters. Ed. David E. Schultz and S. T. Joshi. New York: Hippocampus Press, 2022.

The Notes & Commonplace Book Employed by the Late H. P. Lovecraft Including His Suggestions for Story-Writing, Analyses of the Weird Story, and a List of Certain Basic Underlying Horrors, &c., &c., Designed to Stimulate the Imagination. Ed. R. H. Barlow. Lakeport, CA: The Futile Press, 1938; rpt. West Warwick, RI: Necronomicon Press, 1978.

O Fortunate Floridian: H. P. Lovecraft's Letters to R. H. Barlow. Ed. S. T. Joshi and David E. Schultz. Tampa, FL: University of Tampa Press, 2007; rpt. 2016.

Selected Letters: 1911–1937. Ed. August Derleth and Donald Wandrei (Volumes 1–3); August Derleth and James Turner (Volumes 4–5). Sauk City, WI: Arkham House, 1965–76.

The Shuttered Room and Other Pieces. [Ed. August Derleth.] Sauk City, WI: Arkham House, 1959.

The Spirit of Revision: Lovecraft's Letters to Zealia Brown Reed Bishop. Ed. Sean Branney and Andrew Leman. Glendale, CA: The H. P. Lovecraft Historical Society, 2015.

Works by Others

Barlow, Robert H. Letters to Groo Beck, 1937–38. In private hands.

Baudelaire, Charles. *Les Fleurs du mal.* Trans. Richard Howard. Boston: David R. Godine, 1988.

Bell, Joseph. *Howard Phillips Lovecraft: The Books—Addenda and Auxillary* [*sic*]. Toronto: Soft Books, 1983.

Boerem, R. "The Continuity of the *Fungi from Yuggoth*." *Dark Brotherhood Journal* 1, No. 1 (June 1971): 2–5 (as "On the *Fungi from Yuggoth*"). In Joshi, *H. P. Lovecraft: Four Decades of Criticism*. [222]–25.

Burleson, Donald R. "Scansion Problems in Lovecraft's 'Mirage.'" *Lovecraft Studies* No. 24 (Spring 1991): 18–19, 21. In Burleson's *Lovecraft: An American Allegory: Selected Essays on H. P. Lovecraft*, New York: Hippocampus Press, 2015. 223–28.

Cannon, Peter, ed. *Lovecraft Remembered*. Sauk City, WI: Arkham House, 1998.

Chambers, Robert W. *The Yellow Sign and Other Stories: The Complete Weird Tales*. Ed. S. T. Joshi. [Oakland, CA:] Chaosium, 2000.

de Camp, L. Sprague. *Lovecraft: A Biography*. Garden City, NY: Doubleday, 1975.

Derleth, August, ed. *Dark of the Moon: Poems of Fantasy and the Macabre*. Sauk City, WI: Arkham House, 1947; Freeport, NY: Books for Libraries Press, 1969.

———. Foreword to Lovecraft, *Collected Poems* (q.v.). [3].

Dunsany, Lord. *The Book of Wonder* [and *Time and the Gods*]. New York: Boni & Liveright (Modern Library), [1918]. *LL* 288.

———. *A Dreamer's Tales and Other Stories* [*A Dreamer's Tales* <1910> and *The Sword of Welleran* <1908>]. New York: Boni & Liveright (Modern Library), [1917], [1919], or [1921]. (*LL* 290)

———. *The Gods of Pegāna*. London: Elkin Mathews, [October] 1905. *LL* 293 (HPL's edition unknown).

Ellis, Phillip A. "Unity in Diversity: *Fungi from Yuggoth* as a Unified Setting." *Lovecraft Annual* 1 (2007): 84–90.

Faig, Kenneth W., Jr. "HPL: The Book That Nearly Was." *Xenophile* No. 11 (March 1975): [118]–23.

———. "Lovecraft's Own Book of Weird Fiction." *The* HPL *Supplement* No. 2 (July 1973): 4–15.

———. *Lovecraftian Voyages*. n.p.: Ultratelluric Press, 2013.

———. "A Note Regarding the Harold Farnese Musical Pieces." *Dark Brotherhood Journal* 1, No. 1 (June 1971), 12–14.

———. "R. H. Barlow." In Faig's *The Unknown Lovecraft*. New York: Hippocampus Press, 2009. 194–234.

Fuller, John. *The Sonnet*. London: Methuen, 1972.

Harré, T. Everett, ed. *Beware After Dark!: The World's Most Stupendous Tales of Mystery, Horror, Thrills and Terror.* New York: Macaulay, 1929. *LL* 425.

Hart, Philomena, ed. *The Sideshow of B. K. Hart: A Selection of Columns Written for the* Providence Journal *1929–1941.* Providence: Roger Williams Press, 1941.

Holmes, Olver Wendell. *Elsie Venner: A Romance of Destiny.* Boston: Ticknor & Fields, 1861.

Joshi, S. T. *H. P. Lovecraft: A Comprehensive Bibliography.* Tampa, FL: University of Tampa Press, 2009.

Joshi, S. T., ed. *H. P. Lovecraft: Four Decades of Criticism.* Athens: Ohio University Press, 1980.

———, ed. *H. P. Lovecraft: Four Decades of Criticism.* Athens: Ohio University Press, 1980.

———. *I Am Providence: The Life and Times of H. P. Lovecraft.* 2 volumes. New York: Hippocampus Press, 2010.

———. "Lovecraft's Other Planets." *Crypt of Cthulhu* 4 (Eastertide 1982): 3–11. In Joshi's *Lovecraft and a World in Transition.* New York: Hippocampus Press, 2014. 232–42.

———. "On 'The Book.'" *Nyctalops* 18 (April 1983): 9–13. In Joshi's *Lovecraft and a World in Transition.* New York: Hippocampus Press, 2014. 347–51.

———. "The Poetry of Donald Wandrei." *Studies in Weird Fiction* 3 (Fall 1988): 9–18. Rev. as "Introduction" to Donald Wandrei, *Sanctity and Sin* (q.v.).

———, with David E. Schultz. *Lovecraft's Library.* New York: Hippocampus Press, 2017. Fourth edition, revised and enlarged.

Lord, Glenn. "The Sign of the Dragon-Fly." *Nyctalops* No. 6 (February 1972): 10–11.

Mariconda, Steven J. "Lovecraft's Concept of 'Background.'" *Lovecraft Studies* 5 (Spring 1986): 3–12. In Mariconda's *H. P. Lovecraft: Art, Artifact, and Reality.* New York: Hippocampus Press, 2013. 46–56.

Moe, Maurice W. *Imagery Aids.* Wauwatosa, WI: Kenyon Press, 1931. *LL* 669.

Murray, Will. "Illuminating 'The Elder Pharos.'" *Crypt of Cthulhu* No. 20 (Eastertide 1984): 3–7.

———. "The First Cthulhu Mythos Poem." *Crypt of Cthulhu* No. 20 (Eastertide 1984): 27–29.

Nabokov, Vladimir. *Pale Fire: A Novel.* New York: G. P. Putnam's Sons, 1962.

Price, Robert M. "St. Toad's Hagiography." *Crypt of Cthulhu* No. 9 (Hallowmas 1982): 25–26 (as by "Alonzo Hasbrouck Typer").

———. "'St. Toad's' Revisited." *Crypt of Cthulhu* No. 20 (Eastertide 1984): 21.

———. "St. Toad's Church." In Price's *H. P. Lovecraft and the Cthulhu Mythos.* Mercer Island, WA: Starmont House, 1990: 71–73. Combines the previous two entries.

———. "Second Thoughts on the *Fungi from Yuggoth.*" *Crypt of Cthulhu* No. 78 (St. John's Eve 1991): 3–8.

Rimel, Duane W., and Emil Petaja. "Weird Music." *Phantagraph* 4, No. 4 (July 1936): 6–8. Rpt. *Operation Phantasy,* ed. Donald A. Wollheim. Rego Park, NY: Phantagraph Press, 1967. 24–26.

Schultz, David E. "Following *The Ancient Track.*" *Lovecraft Annual* No. 15 (2021): 46–57.

———. "H. P. Lovecraft's *Fungi from Yuggoth.*" *Crypt of Cthulhu* No. 20 (Eastertide 1984): 3–7. Rpt. *Black Forbidden Things,* ed. Robert M. Price. Mercer Island, WA: Starmont House, 1992. 46–51.

———. "The Lack of Continuity in *Fungi from Yuggoth.*" *Crypt of Cthulhu* No. 20 (Eastertide 1984): 12–16.

Schwartz, Jane. "The Pigeon Game." *Quest/80* 4, No. 9 (July/August 1980): 54.

Scott, Winfield Townley. "A Parenthesis on Lovecraft as Poet." In *Rhode Island on Lovecraft,* ed. Donald M. Grant and Thomas P. Hadley. Providence: Grant–Hadley, 1945. 3–7 (as "Lovecraft as a Poet"). In *H. P. Lovecraft: Four Decades of Criticism,* ed. S. T. Joshi (q.v.). 11–16. In *Lovecraft Remembered,* ed., Peter Cannon (q.v.). 431–35.

Shreffler, Philip A. *The H. P. Lovecraft Companion.* Westport, CT: Greenwood Press, 1977.

Squires, Roy A. *Beyond the Bibliographies.* Catalog 7. Glendale, CA: Roy A. Squires. n.d. [c. 1973].

Teter, George E. *An Introduction to Some Elements of Poetry.* Wauwatosa, WI: Kenyon Press, 1927. LL 951.

Tombaugh, Clyde W., and Patrick Moore. *Out of the Darkness: The Planet Pluto.* Harrisburg, PA: Stackpole Books, 1980.

Vaughan, Ralph E. "The Story in *Fungi from Yuggoth.*" *Crypt of Cthulhu* No. 20 (April 1984): 9–11.

Wandrei, Donald. *Ecstasy and Other Poems.* Athol, MA: Recluse Press, 1928. *LL* 1010.

———. "Lovecraft in Providence." In Lovecraft, *The Shuttered Room* (q.v.). 124–40. In *Lovecraft Remembered,* ed. Peter Cannon (q.v.). 303–17.

———. *Sonnets of the Midnight Hours.*

a. *Weird Tales:*
  1. "The Hungry Flowers." 11, No. 5 (May 1928): 674.
  2. "Dream-Horror" (early version of "In the Pit"). 11, No. 5 (May 1928): 674.
  3. "Purple." 11, No. 6 (June 1928): 837.
  4. "The Eye." 12, No. 1 (July 1928): 69.
  5. "The Grip of Evil Dreams" (early version of "The Old Companions"). 12, No. 2 (August 1928): 231.
  6. "As I Remember" (early version of "The Torturers"). 12, No. 3 (September 1928): 374.
  7. "The Statues." 12, No. 4 (October 1928): 480.
  8. "The Creatures" (early version of "The Prey"). 12, No. 5 (November 1928), 624.
  9. "The Head." 12, No. 6 (December 1928): 815.
  *10. "The Red Spectre." 13, No. 1 (January 1929): 110.
  *11. "Doom." 12, No. 2 (February 1929): 254.
  12. "A Vision of the Future" (early version of "The Ultimate Vision"). 13, No. 3 (March 1929), 420.

*These poems are not in *Sonnets of the Midnight Hours* as it appears in either *Dark of the Moon* or *Poems for Midnight.*

The following collections contain *Sonnets of the Midnight Hours.* It is not certain that Lovecraft read all the poems. The dates of composition of poems that did not appear in *Weird Tales* are unknown, but Lovecraft read the poems in manuscript (see *SL* 2.186).

b. *Dark of the Moon: Poems of Fantasy and the Macabre,* ed. August Derleth. Sauk City, WI: Arkham House, 1947. 380–90. *Contains:* "After Sleep," "Purple," "The Hungry Flowers," "The Eye," "The Torturers," "The Statues," "The Old Companions," "The Head,' "In the Attic," "The Cocoon,"

"The Metal God," "The Little Creature," "The Pool," "The Prey," "The Rack," "Escape," "Capture," "In the Pit," "The Bell," and "The Ultimate Vision."

c. *Poems for Midnight.* Sauk City, WI: Arkham House, 1964. 47–61. *Contains:* "After Sleep," "Purple," "The Old Companions," "The Head," "In the Attic," "The Cocoon," "The Metal God," "The Little Creature," "The Pool," "The Prey," "The Torturers," "The Statues," "The Hungry Flowers," "The Eye," "The Rack," "Escape," "Capture," "In the Pit," "The Unknown Color," "Monstrous Form," "Nightmare in Green," "What Followed Me?," "Fantastic Sculpture," "The Tree," "The Bell," and "The Ultimate Vision."

d. *Collected Poems.* Ed. S. T. Joshi. West Warwick, RI: Necronomicon Press, 1988. 55–69. *Contains: Sonnets of the Midnight Hours* (same selection as in *Poems for Midnight*). Under "Uncollected Poems," there are five additional poems under the heading "Sonnets of the Midnight Hours": "Dream Horror," "The Grip of Evil Dreams," "The Creatures," "The Red Spectre," and "Doom" (75–77), unreprinted since their appearance in *Weird Tales.*

e. *Sanctity and Sin.* Ed. S. T. Joshi. New York: Hippocampus Press, 2008. Rev. ed. of previous item. *Contains: Sonnets of the Midnight Hours* (95–108). Under "Uncollected Poems," the five additional poems are printed under the heading "Sonnets of the Midnight Hours" (123–25).

Waugh, Robert H. "The Structural and Thematic Unity of *Fungi from Yuggoth.*" *Lovecraft Studies* No. 26 (Spring 1992): 2–14. In *Lovecraft: A Century Less a Dream: Selected Criticism on H. P. Lovecraft,* ed. Scott Connors. Holicong, PA: Wildside Press, 2002. 153–77.

Wilson, Edmund. "Tales of the Marvellous and the Ridiculous." *New Yorker* 21, No. 41 (24 November 1945): 100, 103–4, 106. In Wilson's *Classics and Commercials: A Literary Chronicle of the Forties.* New York: Farrar, Straus, 1950; London: W. H. Allen, 1951, 1966; New York: Random House (Vintage Books), 1962; New York: [Book-of-the-Month Club, 1966]; New York: Noonday Press, 1967; Toronto: Ambassador Books, 1967. 286–90. In *H. P. Lovecraft: Four Decades of Criticism,* ed. S. T. Joshi (q.v.). 46–49. In Wilson's *Literary Essays and Reviews of the 1930s and 40s.* New York: Library of America, 2007. 700–703.

Index of Titles and First Lines

Index

Acknowledgments

This book would not be as comprehensive as it is without the interest and generosity of many colleagues.

Greg Belt, Leigh Blackmore, Eric Carlson, R. Alain Everts, S. T. Joshi, Donovan K. Loucks, Steven J. Mariconda, Dirk W. Mosig, R. Dixon Smith, Mark E. Sprague, and Robert E. Weinberg provided copies of the assorted appearances of *Fungi from Yuggoth* from material in their possession. Clair Beck lent me copies of letters written by R. H. Barlow and August Derleth to Beck and his brothers. Robert E. Moe provided a copy of a rare Lovecraft poem from among his father's papers.

R. Boerem, R. Alain Everts, Kenneth W. Faig, Jr., William Fulwiler, S. T. Joshi, Charles Lovecraft, Steven J. Mariconda, Will Murray, and Robert M. Price reviewed various parts of the book in manuscript, sometimes more than once. Their insightful comments and suggestions enriched the Commentary considerably.

Stephan Dziemianowicz, Lloyd Arthur Eshbach, Derrick Hussey, S. T. Joshi, and Donovan K. Loucks also provided assistance in various ways. Christopher Geissler, John H. Stanley, Rosemary Cullen, and the staff of the John Hay Library have provided copies of manuscripts and otherwise assisted me in using the Lovecraft papers. The Wisconsin Historical Society allowed me to consult the August Derleth papers as part of my research.

Thanks also to Dwayne Olson, Michael Waltz, and Dennis Weiler who kindly shared images of Harold Farnese's sheet music for "Mirage" and "The Elder Pharos."

I'm grateful to Jason C. Eckhardt for the thoughtfulness and care he instilled into his art, which evokes the spirit of Lovecraft's poem.

And finally, I must extend special thanks to S. T. Joshi for his unflagging assistance, particularly for performing long-distance research in the 1970s and 1980s at my request, despite his perpetually heavy scholastic workload. The value of his assistance and generosity, on this and so many other projects, cannot be measured, and this book is much richer for his efforts.

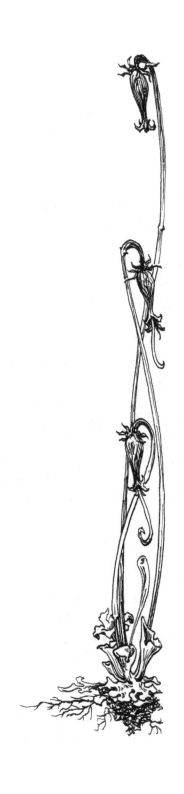

9 780972 164474